THE FIRST MEN IN THE WORLD

By Anne Terry White

Illustrated by E. Harper Johnson

SCHOLASTIC BOOK SERVICES

Published by Scholastic Book Services, a division of Scholastic Magazines, Inc., New York, N. Y.

For Randy and Allen

★   ★   ★

6th printing . . . . January 1967

Printed in the U.S.A.

CONTENTS

1. A Hatchet in the Drift 1
2. "Impossible! Absurd!" 7
3. Is It a Freak? 13
4. An Unwelcome Ancestor Comes to Stay 18
5. The "Missing Link" Appears 26
6. Dragons' Bones 33
7. Deep in the Heart of the Jungle . . . 41
8. "Go On! Seek New Places!" 49
9. Man Against Mammoth 55
10. King of the Ice Age 62
11. Lartet Finds the Reindeer Men . . . 70
12. Bulls on a Ceiling 77
13. Is It a Forgery? 85
14. Bison of Clay 91
15. End of a Hero 98
16. Midnight Magic in a Cave 103
17. Between the Acts 111
18. Enter the Farmer 116
19. Mystery of the Piles 121
20. Stonehenge Goes Up 129
21. Bison Hunt in New Mexico 133
22. Did They Do It All Alone? 138
23. Hats Off! 145
24. On the Shoulders of Stone Age Man . . 149

I wish to express my indebtedness to CHARLES R. KNIGHT and ROY CHAPMAN ANDREWS, whose thinking on prehistoric man has influenced my own.

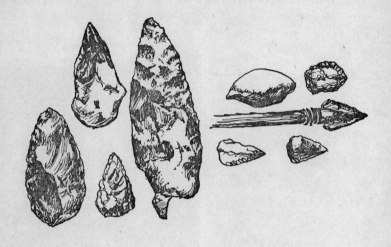

I. A Hatchet in the Drift

On a summer evening in the year 1828 a french-man was walking on the outskirts of the little town of Abbéville. He was deep in thought—so deep that his feet seemed to carry him along of their own accord. Familiarly they took the path up to a gravel pit, made straight for the edge, and stopped there.

The man leaned over. For a long moment he stood looking down on the millions of water-worn pebbles

1

below. Then with a rush and roll of little stones about his ankles, he slid to the bottom.

Stooping, he began at once to rake the gravel lightly with his hand and pick up such stones as were broken. He examined each one with care. Before darkness settled over the gravel pit and forced him to stop, he had examined and dropped hundreds of stones.

"What does Monsieur Boucher de Perthes keep going down into that gravel pit for?" the good folk of Abbéville asked one another. "What can the tax collector find so interesting in a lot of ordinary stones?"

Some shook their heads. Some made circular motions with a finger near the forehead to show it was their opinion Monsieur Boucher de Perthes was not quite right in his head.

But Boucher de Perthes didn't even know that people talked about him. He was completely lost in his thoughts. For he had what is called a "fixed idea."

What was it? What was Boucher de Perthes looking for in the gravel pit?

He was searching for the remains of a Lost Age.

Scholars had divided Man's life on earth into two parts. The first part they called the Age of Bronze. They called it that because the earliest people they knew anything about had made their tools and weapons out of bronze. The other was the Age of Iron. Then, as everybody knew, people made their tools and weapons out of iron.

"But," Boucher de Perthes asked himself, "didn't something come before the Age of Bronze? Surely there must have been a time when Man hadn't yet discovered copper and learned to mix it with tin to make bronze. There must have been an *Age Before Metals*. Well, what did people make their hatchets and knives out of then? Wasn't it stone? If so, can't I find some of those old stone hatchets and knives?"

He thought a great deal about it. He wanted very much to find them. But where should he look?

One evening while he stood by a newly opened gravel pit, it suddenly came to him that right here was a very good place to begin. All afire with the thought, he got down. He picked up one stone and then another. He picked up hundreds, thousands. Alas! Not one looked as if it had been touched by Man. Nature had clearly shaped them all.

But Boucher de Perthes wasn't a man who got easily discouraged. He kept on looking. He looked for years, both there and in a hundred other places.

At last one day in the deposit of sand laid down by the Hôpital River at Abbéville he picked up— right near his own house—a six-inch piece of stone

called flint. It bore just such marks as he was looking for! Two chips had been struck from the edge.
There was no doubt in Boucher de Perthes' mind
that those two chips were the work of Man—Man
who had lived in the Age Before Metals.

He was terribly excited. He couldn't wait to show
his precious flint to a scientist and ran straight to
the nearest one.

The scientist took the flint in his hand, turned it
over a couple of times, then gave it back.

"Monsieur," he said with a smile, "this is the work
of Nature, not Man. Nature, you know, does strange
things sometimes."

Boucher de Perthes took his flint to another scientist. "It is just an accident," the second man said.

All the same Boucher de Perthes went away un-
shaken. He thought he could understand why the
two scientists were so skeptical about his flint. Along
with nearly everybody else in Europe and America,
they believed that Man was a newcomer on earth.
A certain bishop had worked it all out carefully—
the first man, he said, was created in 4004 B.C.
Another important person had even figured out the
exact day and hour it happened—October 23, nine
o'clock in the morning.

Nearly everybody believed in that date. And
nearly everybody, moreover, believed that Man had

come into the world knowing all sorts of practical, everyday things—how to plow and grow grain and keep sheep and cattle and ride on camels. So why shouldn't the two scientists be skeptical about his flint? There was no room on their calendar for any Age of Stone. Nor could they suppose that Man, who was created knowing so much, had ever *needed* to chip flint to make tools and weapons for himself.

Boucher de Perthes was no scientist, but he was the son of a man who had taught him to think for himself. So he stuck to his opinion. And one day, soon afterwards, out of the gravel he pulled a second flint, shaped just like the first. A third flint followed, and it, too, was shaped like the others.

Boucher de Perthes took all three flints to the scientists. "Isn't this sameness of shape proof in it-self?" he demanded. "Surely accident wouldn't make three flints just alike!"

"But it *is* accident," the scientists insisted.

Boucher de Perthes kept on believing. He kept on looking. He even got some laborers to help him look, promising to pay them well if they found any flints like his.

And on a certain day one of the men brought him a flint. It was a stone hatchet. The shape was so clear that anyone could see it was a hatchet. It had come out of a river deposit in a spot not touched

5

before—thirty feet from the surface. This was the best part of it. For from just such a deposit and just such a level huge animal bones had recently been taken. Those bones had been sent to Paris, where the great French scientist Cuvier had pronounced them to be the bones of elephants and rhinoceroses. This flint hatchet, then, must have been made by Man who lived when elephants and rhinoceroses were walking around France! And that was perhaps a hundred thousand years ago!

"Will you please to look at this!" Boucher de Perthes exclaimed triumphantly as he laid the stone hatchet under the scientists' noses.

"Yes, it is a hatchet," they admitted. "But it never came from where you say it did. It couldn't have."

"But just look at the color!" Boucher de Perthes protested. "It is exactly like the color of that river gravel. Look, here is the sand still clinging to the hatchet."

The scientists smiled in a knowing way. "You are really too trustful, Monsieur," they said. "After all, you didn't take the hatchet out of the sand yourself. Nor did you see it taken out. Your laborer has deceived you."

Boucher de Perthes stalked out. Wait! He would show these unbelievers!

2. "Impossible! Absurd!"

BOUCHER DE PERTHES HAD BEEN HUNTING FOR FLINTS pretty steadily for ten years now. But after the scientists turned down his hatchet, he gave himself to the flints entirely.

In all the gravel pits the workmen knew him. For a long time they thought he was crazy and hesitated to work for him. But little by little they got excited about flints themselves. "I will find you a hatchet today, Monsieur," they would call out when they saw him.

Boucher de Perthes took great pains to explain to them just what they ought to look for. "See here," he would say. "Here are a thousand bits of stone. See how Nature has smoothed their edges by rolling them about in the water. Now look at this piece of flint. See how it is shaped. See how a blow has been dealt on this side and on this side to take off a flake and sharpen the flint. It is the hand of Man that has done that."

The workmen learned to recognize the sort of thing he wanted at a glance. And the flints came in. To find his first four flints it had taken Boucher de Perthes nearly ten years. In the next nine he got so many that he had to build a gallery onto his house to hold them.

It was a strange and wonderful museum. It held nearly everything the world knew of the Age Before Metals. Boucher de Perthes' heart swelled as he set his treasures in order. Anyone could see, he thought, how step by step Stone Age Man had learned to use his hands. Some of the flints were rough and crude. Others were shaped perfectly into knives and saws and hammers. He had hatchets of stone with handles of stag horn. He had boxes dug out of the kneecaps of oxen. He had javelins made out of bone and hardened in the fire.

It took endless hours to arrange the treasures.

For Boucher de Perthes wanted each object to have a ticket attached to it, telling where and how it had been found. Beside each thing, moreover, he set a sample of the earth from which it had been taken.

At last all was ready. Boucher de Perthes opened his doors. He let it be known that any passing stranger was welcome to enter and examine everything.

The trouble was that strangers didn't pass that way very often. That bothered the collector. Oughtn't he to send his collection to Paris where all the world came to visit? He would write to a museum and offer to send them everything he had.

To his astonishment the museum would have nothing to do with his flints and stones and bones. Paris didn't believe in his Age of Stone. It didn't believe there had been men on earth before the Bronze Age. His collection was a fraud, a pack of nonsense, and he could keep it.

Boucher de Perthes was taken aback. How could people be so blind? It seemed to him there were such powerful reasons to believe Man had been on earth before the Age of Bronze. Scientists knew from the bones that were always being dug up out of the river drift that once very different kinds of mammals lived on earth. They had all perished, in a great flood doubtless. They had become extinct— not one such animal roamed the earth today. Well,

9

wasn't it reasonable to suppose that there had once been a different kind of Man and that he, too, had become extinct?

Boucher de Perthes sat down and wrote a book about his ideas and sent it to the Academy of Arts and Sciences in Paris. He drew pictures of the different things he had found and put them into the book, too.

The learned gentlemen in the Academy turned the pages of the heavy book. They read the arguments and looked at the drawings. They felt very uncomfortable. They didn't like ideas that upset what science and religion taught. Who was this Boucher de Perthes anyway? A nobody from Abbéville. His ideas were wild, simply wild.

Some who read the book said merely, "He is a dreamer." Others said, "He is a madman, a madman who swears all the world is mad."

It was all very disappointing.

Now of all the people who read Boucher de Perthes' book, the one who most often called him madman was a certain Dr. Rigollot of Amiens. This man was forever going around with the words "Impossible! Absurd!" on his lips. Very likely he would have gone to his grave saying them were it not for a friend of his who had by chance paid a visit to

Boucher de Perthes' museum. One day the friend buttonholed Dr. Rigollot.

"Come along. I want you to see Boucher de Perthes' things for yourself," he said. "Just do me the favor, please."

To humor his friend, Dr. Rigollot let himself be dragged along. He thought he'd go in, take a quick look around, and come out with even better reasons to say "Impossible! Absurd!" Instead, he found himself walking around the gallery in utter amazement.

"I am in another world!" he exclaimed over and over again as he examined the hatchets, the knives, the boxes. "They are certainly man-made. One would have to be blind to deny it!"

After he had looked everything over, Dr. Rigollot held out his hand to Boucher de Perthes. "I have done you a great injustice, Monsieur," the doctor said. "But words alone will never set things right. I will help you to get recognition for Man of the Age of Stone."

No sooner did he get back to Amiens than Rigollot started out to examine river deposits. And, as with Boucher de Perthes, everything else went out of his head. He, too, started running around. He, too, wanted to tell everybody about flints and bones and

Stone Age Man who had lived in France along with elephants and rhinoceroses.

But all the good doctor's talking and writing were just so much effort wasted. People didn't want to hear of any Age of Stone.

"We'll believe in the things your Stone Age Man made when you show us the man himself," they said. "People keep finding the remains of animals of that time. If Man also existed then, show us his bones!"

"Have patience!" Boucher de Perthes replied. *"He will be found.* Look at how many of his works have come into our hands. Is it not clear from the number of flints and worked bones remaining to us that Man was numerous in the Age of Stone? Yes, not one but many skeletons of Stone Age Man will be found!"

3. Is It a Freak?

STONE AGE MAN! WHAT A PROBLEM HE WAS! HOW
much easier it was to believe that Boucher de
Perthes and Dr. Rigollot had invented him just to
get in the papers. Even the few people who believed
the two Frenchmen were honest hoped their Stone
Age Man would never be found. It would be so
embarrassing if he were. And so unpleasant. It
would mean people would have to admit Man was

an animal, a very intelligent animal, instead of a being specially created to rule over bird, beast, and fish!

They put Stone Age Man out of their minds. Please heaven his bones would never be found.

But the prayer was in vain.

In western Germany there is a river called Dussel. It has not always flowed where it does today. The Dussel has cut its way down and has left behind a beautiful little gorge with a limestone cliff on one side.

In the year 1856 some men were quarrying limestone in this Neanderthal gorge and had reached a little cave about sixty feet above the stream. The floor of the cave, they found, was covered with mud several feet deep. So two workmen were set to clearing it out.

They were busily working away at it when four or five feet down, near the entrance, they came upon the top part of a skull. There wasn't any face to it and no jaw. What kind of creature it had belonged to they couldn't guess, but anyway they had no time to waste on bones. They threw the skullcap out along with the mud. When a little later they came to some more bones lying on the same level, they threw them out also.

That night, however, they happened to mention

they had found bones in the cave, and somehow the story got to the owner of the quarry.

"I want those bones saved," he ordered.

Accordingly the next day the workmen brought him the skullcap and some of the larger bones— fourteen pieces in all. The quarry owner looked them over and shrugged his shoulders. He didn't know what creature they had belonged to either.

Now it happened by good fortune that in the town of Elberfeld next door there lived a man who was interested in caves and whatever could be found in them. He had all the time been keeping an eye on the men who were quarrying the limestone, and when he heard about the bones, he asked for them. He no sooner laid eyes on them than he knew he had got hold of something extraordinary. The skull especially excited him. The forehead was very low and slanting, and above the eye sockets there were enormous brow-ridges. They jutted out and stretched without a break from one side of the head to the other. Now what kind of animal had brow-ridges like that?

"With your permission," the man from Elberfeld said to the quarry owner, "I'll ship these bones to Professor Schaafhausen in Bonn. He is an expert in bones. He is sure to be interested in them. He will tell us what they are."

Professor Schaafhausen was quite definitely interested. In fact, he said they were the most interesting bones he had ever seen in his life. He studied them from every possible angle. And he came out with a statement.

"They are the bones of Man, and they are very, very old."

Man? That forehead? Those horrible projecting brow-ridges? Those beast-like ribs?

Yes, Man!

What a to-do there was! People just couldn't bring themselves to believe they had had such an unflattering ancestor.

One scientist suggested the Neanderthal skull had most likely belonged to some silly hermit who had shut himself up in the cave to get away from the temptations of this world. Another said the skull was that of a Russian Cossack. People grasped at any straw. When at last a very big authority stepped forward and said it was the skull of an idiot, a sigh of relief went up.

"That's what it is, of course! It is the skull of an idiot!" people repeated with joy. "That's what those brow-ridges mean. The man had a diseased brain."

"Nonsense!" an important English authority retorted. "Apes have brow-ridges like that. Would you say that all apes have diseased brains because they have brow-ridges?"

That set people back for a moment. But they weren't going to give up everything they had been taught just because somebody gave them a sound argument.

"You can't tell anything from just one skull," they said. "You have no right to say there was a race of men with brow-ridges like that till you find other skeletons having the same kind of brow-ridges."

After they said it, they felt much better. Secretly they hoped no more skeletons with brow-ridges would be found. How nice it would be if the man from the Neanderthal who was causing all this trouble proved to be a freak!

4. An Unwelcome Ancestor
Comes to Stay

PROFESSOR SCHAAFHAUSEN HAD SAID THE NEANDER-
thal bones were very, very old. But how old was
very, very old?

Nobody knew.

Could it be that these Neanderthal bones were
those of a man of the Age Before Metals?

One of the scientists most interested in finding out was the Englishman Hugh Falconer. He knew more about the bones of animals such as no longer exist than anyone else in the world. He could tell from a single tooth what kind of animal it had belonged to.

On one of his trips to Paris, Falconer had met Boucher de Perthes and received from him a copy of his book. Hugh Falconer didn't think much of it. However, it happened that in his travels to look at old bones he found himself one day in Abbéville. He thought he'd look in on Boucher de Perthes' museum. And what a shock he got!

He sat down at once and wrote a letter to his scientist friends in England. "I strongly recommend that you come to Abbéville. I am sure you will be richly rewarded."

Two of them dashed across the Channel. They hadn't been in the museum an hour before it was clear to them as to Falconer that they would have to change their views. They had believed that Man appeared on the stage just yesterday. Why, he stretched back so far that no one could see his beginning.

Their thoughts jumped naturally to the Neanderthal Man. Was it he who had made the flint tools in Boucher de Perthes' museum? Had Man with the brow-ridges lived at the same time as the extinct mammals?

There was just one way to find out. Someone would have to dig up a skeleton like the one from the Neanderthal cave *together with bones of extinct mammals*. That would be proof positive that the man and the animals had lived at the same time.

Would anyone ever do that?

A lot of people tried. A lot of caves were explored. But years passed and nobody succeeded in digging up another skeleton with brow-ridges.

Most people, of course, were very happy about that. They could go on believing that the man from the Neanderthal was a freak. For thirty years they went on saying, "I told you so." Then something happened that took the wind out of their sails.

On the estate of the Count de Beaufort in the district of Spy in Belgium there was a small cave that had from time to time attracted attention. Several people had dug around in it and found quite a few pieces of nicely worked flint and bones. The Count was very generous about letting people explore his cave. When in 1885 two Belgian scientists asked to dig, he at once said, "Go ahead."

As a matter of fact, Marcel de Puydt and Max Lohest didn't care to dig in the cave itself. They intended to explore the unturned earth just in front of it. For they strongly suspected that the large terrace in front of the cave had been lived on and had perhaps been used even more than the cave itself. The terrace was many feet higher than the cave floor so that you had to step down to get in. "Maybe," they thought, "the reason why the terrace is higher is that dirt and litter have piled up on it."

The two scientists had dug before. They knew from experience that in far-off times people didn't worry about cleanliness the way folks do nowadays. The people of the dim past didn't bother to sweep or pick up. They let litter lie where it fell. They let it stay there generation after generation and century after century till they lived on what we would call a dump. Maybe the high terrace at Spy was such a dump. If it was, what might they not find there?

Very carefully they began to sink a trench.

In the uppermost layer, of course, they didn't expect to find anything because they knew that for some time no human beings had lived in the cave. The top layer was not Man's dirt. The bits of limestone had fallen from the rock above. The dust had been blown on the terrace by the winds. Still, as they dug down, they realized that even the empty top layer had a story to tell them. For it was more

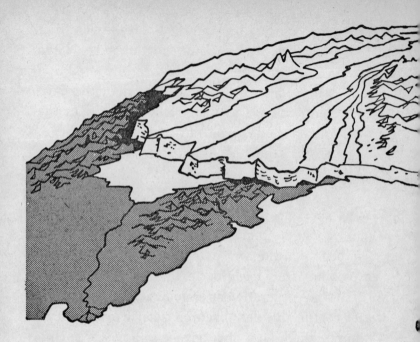

than nine feet thick. What thousands upon thousands of years must have passed since cave dwellers had last set foot here!

Patiently they dug down through the nine feet and started on the next layer. And now signs of life began to appear. Bones of mammoth and deer showed up; long, narrow flints showed up. Man had surely lived here, but for how long they couldn't tell.

Down into the next layer they dug. It was deep red in color and harder to get through. But it was

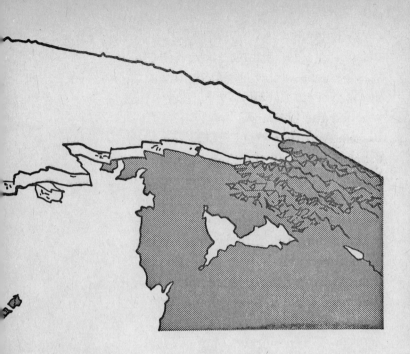

chock-full of treasure. Thousands of flints, ruder than those in the second layer and of a quite different shape, were there. Bits of charcoal were there, pieces of ivory, arrowheads made of bone, chips of pottery.

And wonderful animal bones. A few were of creatures such as still roam the world today. But most were of animals long extinct. Everything was solidly welded together, covering what lay below like a crust.

And what did lie below?

With great curiosity the scientists dug on. But disappointingly little showed up. The layer, which was of yellow clay, seemed to have nothing in it at all. Not till they got down through six inches and reached the bottom of the clay did they find a sign of life. And that was nothing but a streak of wood ashes. Clearly all the time the yellow clay was collecting on the terrace, nobody had lived there or in the cave.

Was this the end then?

Down into the fifth layer they cut. More bones of extinct animals just as in the third layer. And then—was it true or were they dreaming?—bones that were quite different, bones that to their trained eyes spelled MAN!

Quite a large part of a human skeleton was there. It lay on its side, the hand touching the lower jaw. A few feet away lay the scattered bones of a second human skeleton.

With trembling hands the scientists picked out the first skull. It was thick and heavy. The low forehead sloped sharply back. Over the eye sockets there was a projecting ridge of bone that went straight across from one side of the head to the other.

De Puydt and Lohest exchanged a meaningful glance. They knew this fellow. It was their old friend of the Neanderthal cave.

The great question was settled, then—the Neanderthaler was not an idiot, was not a freak. He and the Spy men were simply human beings of another kind. They were men of the Stone Age. Perhaps they were the fellows whom Falconer and his British scientist friends so longed to see.

What an ocean of ink was spilled now! What a deal of talk there was! It was hard, hard. But it looked as if people would have to accept the fact that they were not the one and only, created to rule over all that lived and breathed. Another kind of Man had walked the earth before them. And he was by no means such an ancestor as they would have chosen.

Why, the scientists said he didn't even stand quite straight, that always he had his knees a little bit bent. And that terrible head and face like an ape's. Oh, they didn't want him, they just didn't want him. What wouldn't they give to have back the good old days before Neanderthal Man was discovered!

5. The "Missing Link" Appears

BUT NOBODY COULD TURN THE CLOCK BACK. NEANDER-
thal Man had come, and after Spy it was certain he
was going to stay. Gone were the days when scientists could dismiss the Stone Age with a wave of
the hand, when they could rattle off the day and
year Man appeared on earth.

Indeed, many scientists had stopped believing

Man had been suddenly created at all. They had come to think that he had slowly developed from some ape-like ancestor who had lived long before Neanderthal Man. In their mind's eye they saw this mysterious creature. He was neither ape nor Man, but something in between.

They talked a great deal about him. They called him the "missing link"; for they pictured Man's story on earth as a sort of broken chain. The last link in the chain was Homo *sapiens*, Man as we know him today. Somewhere down the middle was Neanderthal Man. And over at the other end was the unknown creature, not Man, not ape.

Now the person who thought and talked about the "missing link" most of all was a young Dutch surgeon by the name of Eugene Dubois. The "missing link" was his "fixed idea." Indeed, thinking and talking about the mysterious, unknown being was not enough. Eugene Dubois finally got to the point where he simply had to go and look for him. He had a theory as to the place where he would be most likely to find the Ape-Man's bones.

That place was the group of large islands off the coast of India. He reasoned it out like this: "Those islands are the home of two of the manlike apes. The gibbon lives in Java, Sumatra, and Borneo. The orang makes his home in the last two. Isn't it likely that I will find the 'missing link' in a region where apes abound?"

Dubois had another reason, too. He had read that great beds of animal bones had just been found in Java. "Now among those bones . . ." he thought.

He made no secret of his plan. Naturally his friends, to whom it seemed utterly crazy, said everything they could to stop him. But they couldn't change the surgeon's mind.

"Don't worry about me," he said. And throwing up his job, he enlisted in the Medical Corps of the Dutch Army. "I'll bring home the 'missing link.'" That was his last word as the ship sailed off to Sumatra. The year was 1887.

But it is one thing to have an idea, another to carry it out. It didn't take Dubois long to find out that army doctors don't have much time for digging. In two years all he could do in that line was explore a few caves. He was beginning to think he had made a fool of himself when one day he was called to headquarters. The Dutch Government wanted to find out more about the bone beds in Java. Did Dubois want to undertake the job?

The young doctor jumped at the chance. "I have been dreaming of those bones night and day," he said.

But even his dreams, he was to find out, couldn't match the real thing. When Dubois got to the spot and saw the steep bank of the Solo River with bones sticking right out of the sandstone, he thought he was in Paradise. Years of wonderful work were ahead of him. Now in the dry season the stream was forty-five feet below the bank. He would have to explore all that and more. What wonderful adventures were before him! And always there was the great chance that he would stumble on what he had come so far to find.

He began to dig. Day after day and month after month he worked down through the forty-five feet. By 1891 he had got to the level of the stream. And now he saw that all the thrills above were as nothing compared to what he would get below. In the next four feet the bones lay thick as plums in a plum pudding, and each bone was a gem. He recognized the extinct hippopotamus, rhinoceros, hyena, elephant, pig, lion. Before long he had taken from this one layer the bones of twenty-seven different kinds of mammals, most of them extinct.

Often as he worked Dubois would try to picture to himself the story of this wonderful natural history museum. Perhaps it was a quarter of a million years ago. Perhaps it was more. But ages ago this river bank, he knew, had been the bottom of the then nameless Solo River. Afterwards, along with all this region, the river had been slowly lifted up. Then the stream, seeking a way to the sea, had had to cut down through its own deposits. They stood now as banks high above it, telling Nature's story to all who knew her language.

As for the bones, they were the living part of the story. They were what remained of all the lush animal life that went on around the river those thousands upon thousands of years ago.

Dubois took pleasure in putting flesh on the dry, dead bones. He could see the great, plant-eating creatures coming down to the river to drink and swim and play. He could see the flesh-eaters stealing down to hunt them. There had been tragedies. Screams had resounded, teeth and claws had ripped through flesh, blood had flowed. Dead bodies had fallen into the water, bones had been washed in from the bank. Then sand had covered them up. Mud from a volcano had flowed over them. Then more sand had gathered. And so it had gone on and on, century after century, thousands upon other thousands of years.

As he thought of these things, one question was ever in the doctor's mind. Had there been amongst all the creatures that came down to the river in that long ago one that walked on two feet? . . .

Every single day Dubois hoped the next bone would be that of the "missing link."

And then one day it happened. In the palm of his hand there lay a tooth different from any he had ever seen. Its roots were wide apart as in the apes, but its crown was human—an Ape-Man might well have had a tooth like that!

Dubois' heart skipped a couple of beats. Beside all the huge bones he had dug up, this one little tooth looked so insignificant! Yet to him it was worth all the rest. It shot his hopes sky-high. Surely somewhere among the countless bones in this rich layer lay the rest of the skeleton!

Days and weeks passed. Then one morning, two or three feet from the place where he found the tooth, he picked out a large, ape-like skull. It felt very heavy in his hand. It was chocolate brown in color and harder than marble. The forehead was very low and sloping. Above the eye sockets was a heavy ridge of bone such as gorillas have.

Was this the skull of the Ape-Man? Or did it belong to an extinct ape? But then, why was it so large? Surely this skull had held a brain too large for an ape. Why, the creature's brain must have been two-thirds the size of an average human brain.

Carefully Dubois compared his find with the skull of gorilla and chimpanzee, orangutan, gibbon, and Man. He couldn't make up his mind. Was it ape? Or was it Man?

Then he thought, "After all, the thing that distinguishes Man most from all other mammals is that he walks erect. If I could find the leg bones, I would know. I would be able to tell whether this creature had stood upright or not."

He worked and he hoped. In August of 1892, forty feet from the place where he had found the skull, he picked up a long, straight thigh bone.

Now he knew. On this thigh bone a creature as tall as a modern human being had walked erect. The skull had belonged to an early Man. What should he name this new-found link in the human chain? Wouldn't *Pithecanthropus erectus,* the Erect Ape-Man, describe him best of all?

6. Dragons' Bones

THERE HAD BEEN TALK, TALK, TALK WHEN NEAN-
derthal Man was discovered. But it was nothing to
what went on when Eugene Dubois brought the
bones of his Ape-Man home from Java. The head-
lines screamed: *"Missing Link" Found at Last*.
And fast as lightning the news sped around the
globe. People everywhere read it with open mouths
and sinking hearts.

Dreadful, dreadful! Here they had barely recov-
ered from the shock of Neanderthal Man, and now

a much worse ancestor had sprung from the earth to plague them. "*Supposed to have lived a quarter of a million to half a million years ago,*" they read. "*Claimed to be proof positive that Man has climbed up from the ape.*" Dreadful and worse than dreadful!

But wait! Not so fast! Scientists weren't all of one opinion! In England, to be sure, they had opened their arms to the Ape-Man. But in Germany nearly all were certain the bones couldn't be a man's.

Couldn't be a monkey's. Couldn't be a man's. Such a war of words raged about the bones that poor Dubois was bewildered. He went here and he went there. He took the Ape-Man's bones from Holland to France, to Ireland, Scotland, England, Germany, Austria. Everywhere he showed them there was the same talk, talk, talk. "It's a monkey! It's a man!" Finally it got to be too much for the surgeon. He packed the bones up, went home to Amsterdam, put them in a strong box under his bed, and shut himself up in his house. For three years he stayed there. He wouldn't let anybody look at the bones.

But that didn't stop the talk. And when after three years Dubois brought them out again, things became hotter and hotter. It got so that Dubois himself didn't know any more what he thought. Sometimes he thought *Pithecanthropus* was an ape, sometimes he thought he was a man.

"What we need to settle this is more bones," the scientists said.

Who would find them? An expedition went off to Java. But all the human bones it brought back was one tooth, picked up about two miles from the spot where Dubois had found his *Pithecanthropus*.

Was the story to be left hanging in the air then? Not by any means.

In the year 1899 a German naturalist, K. A. Haberer by name, had gone out to China to explore the interior. He was a man whose curiosity led him everywhere, and one day it took him into a Chinese druggist's shop. A drawer in the druggist's cabinet was standing open. To his surprise Haberer saw that it was filled with all sorts of teeth and bones.

"What are these for?" he asked the druggist.

"Medicine," the druggist replied. "These are dragons' teeth and dragons' bones. There is great power in them. I will grind them to a powder and it will be fine medicine to cure spasms and madness and gallstones. Dragons' bones are very good for malaria, too. And paralysis. Also liver trouble."

Now Haberer knew that in China people didn't

think of the dragon as a wicked monster but rather as people's friend and protector. So when he heard that powdered dragon bones made very good medicine, the naturalist wasn't too surprised.

However, to him the dragons' bones looked remarkably like the bones of extinct animals. He bought quite a few, then went into another shop and bought some more. Afterwards he packed the whole business up in a box and sent it along with a letter to a scientist in Germany.

What a thrill Haberer got when the bones proved to be the remains of mammals which ages ago had lived in China! There were ninety different kinds of them.

Of course, all sorts of people besides Haberer wanted to know what place in China the bones had come from. But the Chinese druggists wouldn't tell anybody where they got their dragons' bones. For years they kept the secret till at last a druggist in Peking gave it away. He got his dragons' bones, he said, from a market in Chichou.

Well, that was a help. It meant that the bones must come from somewhere up on the Yellow River. J. Gunnar Andersson, Mining Adviser to the Chinese Government, got on the trail immediately and before long found himself in the very heart of the dragons' bone country.

What a sight met his eyes! Bones, bones, bones. Everywhere Andersson went he saw people digging bones. The strongest place of all was the village of Chi Chia Kou. It was a regular mining town, with a great network of tunnels and galleries going deep down under the ground. "There are bones enough here to fill all the museums in the world," Andersson thought and lost no time getting the miners to collect for him.

Dragons' bones had led him to a wonderful adventure. But Chi Chia Kou was just the beginning.

About thirty miles southwest of Peking, there stood at that time a curious little hill called Chicken Bone Hill. Now any name that had the word *bone* in it interested Andersson. So in the year 1918 he went out to look at the hill. One glance showed him that it was the inside of a cave! The limestone on the outside had been quarried away and the dirt and other things that had collected inside the cave had been left standing.

"Somebody ought to explore Chicken Bone Hill," he thought and went away planning to do it.

But dragons' bones somewhere else kept Andersson so busy that it was three years before he came back to show the hill to an American scientist. By that time an Austrian was already on the spot digging. He was getting a lot of bird bones out, and, of course, started to tell Andersson and the American about them.

They were sitting there, discussing dragons' bones, when all of a sudden a Chinese voice startled them. A stranger was standing before them.

"There is no use staying here any longer," he said. "Not far from here there is a place where you can collect much larger and better dragons' bones. I will show you."

Full of curiosity the three men followed the Chinese, who led them northward, northward, over the limestone hills till they came to a steep wall of limestone about thirty feet high.

"There," the stranger said and pointed out a cleft in the wall.

Climbing up, they found themselves in a huge cave with a fallen-in roof. They began to dig and almost at once came on the jaw of a pig.

Now what would a pig be doing in a cave? Andersson found it hard to tear himself from the riddle. He went off vowing he'd be back—and very soon he was.

It was on this return visit that he got a hint of the cave's secret. In his absence the scientists had got together quite a little pile of bones—rhino, hyena, bear, and so on. Andersson naturally went over to examine them. But it wasn't bones that he picked up to look at. Some little flakes of quartz with very sharp edges drew his eye.

"Where did these come from?" he asked.

"Found them right along with the bones," one of the scientists answered.

Andersson was puzzled. The quartz flakes didn't naturally belong in the cave. How had they got in? He couldn't help feeling that those sharp flakes of quartz had been *carried* in. Now, animal bones could be carried in by a beast of prey. But what creature would carry in flakes of quartz? Was it possible that a man creature had lived in the cave and used these flakes to cut things with?

Suddenly the mining expert remembered something that all the time had been sleeping in the back of his mind. He remembered that among the dragons' bones Haberer had sent to Germany there was one tooth that had stumped the scientist. "Is this the tooth of Man?" the scientist had asked. He couldn't tell. It was like, yet unlike, any human teeth he had ever seen.

Andersson thought of that tooth and stared at the sharp quartz flakes. A queer sensation shot through him—he felt as though he stood on the edge of discovery. Knocking solemnly on the wall of the cave, he said to the scientists, "I have a feeling that in this cave lie the remains of one of our ancestors. It is only a question of your finding him. Take your time. Stick to it till the cave is emptied if need be."

The two scientists gave a wry smile. It was easy to say "till the cave is emptied." Why, the digging now was getting so difficult and dangerous that before long they'd have to quit. Any moment the roof might fall in some more.

"We'll stick it out till the end of the summer," they said.

Andersson was heartbroken. The chips of quartz had taken such hold of his imagination that he couldn't rest till he knew how they had got in the cave. After the scientists gave up, he chafed and chafed. For two years he suffered.

"Go back," he pleaded with the Austrian scientist. "Dig a little more."

The Austrian finally agreed. And this time when he left the cave he had two teeth of a human creature!

There was no holding Andersson down now. He was more excited over the two teeth than over his whole huge collection of dragons' bones. For his hunch had been proved right. The ancestor he had predicted was found—Peking Man had been added to the human family.

7. Deep in the Heart of the Jungle

OF COURSE, TWO TEETH AREN'T MUCH TO BUILD A
man on. Scientists the world over waited to see what
else would come out of the cave of Chou Kou Tien.
And in time they saw.

First came another human tooth.

Then came a whole nest of Man's bones, including twenty teeth and parts of skulls.

And finally came the most wonderful find of all—a brain case not quite, but almost, whole.

Nobody could say any more that Andersson had made a fool of himself. For now his Peking Man was 100 per cent proved. Only the creature had been given another name now. *Sinanthropus* scientists called him—Man of China.

"But what did he look like, your Man of China?" people asked while experts fussed with the bones, trying to make a portrait bust of him.

"Well," they replied, "he had a great ridge of bone jutting out over his eyes like a shelf. And almost no forehead. He was an amazingly low type. Much like the Java Ape-Man. We can't get over how much like Dubois' Ape-Man he was. The two must have lived about the same time—a quarter or half a million years ago."

"Like Dubois' Ape-Man, you say? Then it wasn't a monkey?"

"Oh, definitely not. That thigh bone he found was a monkey's and so were the teeth. But the skullcap was a man's all right. Why, the Java Ape-Man had a brain nearly as good as our *Sinanthropus* here. And *he* assuredly was a man."

"But Dubois himself now thinks *Pithecanthropus* was a monkey!"

It was the truth. Dubois had changed his mind. He didn't believe in any of his bones any more.

What were people to think? Would the pesky question never be settled for good? Here it was 1937, nearly fifty years since Dubois had made his find, and still the scientists were arguing; "Is it a monkey? Is it a man?"

But now the answer was just around the corner. That same year another Dutchman started finding so many Ape-Man bones in Java that the whole argument fell apart. After what Von Koeningswald got out of the bone beds, nobody could say that Dubois' Ape-Man was a monkey.

In fact, the new finds proved not only that *Pithecanthropus* was a real man; they showed that, like the three bears in the story, he had come in three different sizes. There had been a Little Ape-Man, a Middle-Sized Ape-Man, and a Great Big Ape-Man. The Middle-Sized Ape-Man had been about as big as a full grown male gorilla. And the Great Big Ape-Man was truly a giant.

A giant! How big?

Well, very big. One of his lower back teeth measured seven-eighths of an inch across. His jaw was so big that a modern man's jaw looks like a baby's beside it. The fellow must have been over seven feet tall and big in proportion. Perhaps he weighed around 750 pounds.

And did the three Ape-Men live together?

Certainly not! They most likely didn't even live at the same time. The Great Big Ape-Man probably came first, and the chances are he came from China. At least, that's what the scientists think because, in among dragons' bones in the drug shops of Hong Kong, Von Koeningswald found three of the giant's teeth. Maybe the Middle-Sized Ape-Man developed from the giant. But anyway the Ape-Men got smaller and smaller till they weren't any bigger than five feet or so. That's how tall the Man of China was, and the chances are that his close kin in Java was about the same.

No, the Little Ape-Man wasn't very big, and by our measure he wasn't very smart, but oh, he was Man. And that's saying a very great deal.

For look at him—there he stands erect on his two feet. He can walk around all day on those wonderful feet of his and not get tired. Never, never does he have to put his hands on the ground to help himself along the way an ape has to. No, his hands are free, absolutely free. And they are wonderful hands. The thumb not only can be folded over toward the fingers so he can grasp. It is much longer than in the apes. With that thumb he can get a really good grip. He can take a heavy stone and pound hard. He can take a sharp stone and cut with it. He can pick up a stick and strike a smashing blow with it.

And just listen to him! He can talk, he calls things by name. He can tell someone what he wants, what he knows, what he imagines. The rest of the mammals make sounds, but they never, never speak. Sometimes when he meets his cousin the orang in the jungle, *Pithecanthropus* speaks to him. The ape makes a face at him but doesn't say a word. Why doesn't he answer?

Why doesn't he? There is no reason—except that he hasn't the brains to do it. He has a voice box. He could talk if he wanted to. But he hasn't brains enough to want to. He just makes noises. He just makes faces. He jumps up and down when he's angry. But he doesn't say anything.

Warily the Ape-Man picks his way through the jungle; for there is always danger around. Big, lion-like creatures and hyenas are forever looking for a chance to nab him. Sometimes when he hears a frightening sound the Ape-Man climbs a tree. Sometimes he picks up a stick or stone to defend himself with. Most often he runs away. For he hasn't any good weapons yet. One of these days his descendants will think of sharpening a stick to a point and hardening it in the fire to make a real spear. He hasn't thought of that.

But already he knows fire. It is no longer a dread enemy from which he runs away. He has learned to handle it, to feed it with dry wood, to quench it with water. Fire is his friend and he can never get over the wonder of it or ever be grateful enough that it is his.

Sometimes when he puts a chunk of meat on a stick and holds it in the flames, he remembers the day he captured fire. The whole jungle was ablaze that day—was it lightning or the volcano that had started it? They had run, run, and the fire had run after them. All the creatures of the jungle had made for the river. Fire was strong, but water was stronger and killed the fire.

Afterwards there had been a wonderful smell in the air. He had crept back through the charred jungle. There in a heap of smoldering ashes lay a tapir dead, and the wonderful smell was rising out of it. How he had gorged himself on the smoking flesh! Then he had bethought himself; "Fire has done this." Cautiously he had picked up a burning stick and carried it home. And fire had become his friend. Now it roasts his meat and in bad weather

keeps him warm. He doesn't let the fire run away
and set the jungle ablaze.

Deep in the heart of that jungle he has built
himself a shelter. It isn't much of a house—just a
roof of palm leaves woven clumsily together with
grasses and fibers and supported on sticks stuck
in the ground. There aren't any sides. It's just a roof
to keep the rain off. Under it he and his family can
stay fairly dry while the rain streams down.

They sit there huddled with their arms around
one another to keep warm—and dream of food.
When the sun comes out and the dripping jungle is
dry again, they will creep out to gather fruits and
nuts, to dig roots and steal birds' eggs out of their
nests. Perhaps with a lucky blow of his stick the
Ape-Man will kill some small animal or some care-
less bird sitting on a low branch. Maybe he will find
a dead creature torn and half eaten by its enemy.
Meat! What a wonderful thing meat is! He doesn't
get it very often.

If only he were strong enough to kill the really
big animals the way they kill one another! Then
he could bring meat home every day. But he has
no claws to tear with, no fangs to bite with, no hoofs
to stamp with, no horns, no tusks to toss with—and
no fur to protect him. Instead of claws and fangs he
has to use sticks and stones. He has to use his brains.

And the animals are so large and so fierce. The elephants, rhinos, buffalos, and hippopotami are beyond his strength to kill. The tapir is big as a horse.

He has to use his brains. And he does use them; he likes to think. Just as Man hundreds of thousands of years later will enjoy doing, so he likes to sit by the fire and think and work things out in his head. He is curious as a monkey about everything, but unlike a monkey he is curious with a purpose.

For he is Man. He wants to know, to do, to have, to be.

8. "Go On! Seek New Places!"

MORE AND MORE SURPRISES KEPT COMING OUT OF THE
cave of Chou Kou Tien. By 1945 bones belonging
to forty or so different people—grownups and
children—had been taken out. The scientists didn't
let anything in the cave escape them. They studied
even what had been Man's garbage to see what kind
of plant food he had eaten. And out of all the dead
things came a living picture—a picture of Man as
he stepped out of the jungle.

How did the story go?

Often and often Man stood on the jungle's edge

and peered through the bushes at the sunlit plain beyond. He was not used to so much brightness. He was excited by so much space. There was something about space that lifted him up, that made him want to run and shout. In the jungle he must always pick his way cautiously on account of the roots and vines that trip and the enemies that lurk behind every bush. But here everything is open. Dazzling sunshine is over everything.

Sometimes he would venture—hesitantly, fearfully—into the open, and a sense of well-being would flow through him. He liked the warm sunshine on his naked body. But at the first sound of danger he would scamper back into the jungle. With all its terrors, the jungle was home. Had not Man always lived there? Were not the trees his safety?

Once as he sat sunning himself on the jungle's edge he saw death overtake a hoofed creature of the plain. The animal had wandered from its fellows and stood quietly feeding in the tall grass when suddenly a yellow streak shot through the air. Straight on the creature's back the tiger landed. Monstrous claws dug in, saber-teeth stabbed again and again. The plains creature had reared and plunged, trying to shake off the terrible burden. But it was all over in a little while. Afterwards when the killer had gone to sleep off his meal, Man had stolen to the kill. With a sharp stone he had cut off a huge chunk of meat and two long bones and carried them home.

Another time his curiosity had overcome his fear. The shining river tempted him. He had crept through the high grass to the water and had lain there on the bank watching the small finny creatures that swam about. He had put his hands into the shallow stream and after many tries had caught a brightly striped fish. It had squirmed and flapped about as he held it, but he had eaten it raw. After that, many times he went to the river to catch the slow-moving, unwary creatures.

Sometimes when he lay by the stream and looked beyond, he would see a herd of antelope leaping in the distance. They filled him with a strange sense of envy. He, too, wanted to leap and run across the open plain. Restlessness and discontent would take hold of him. He was so tired of the dismal jungle where the sun just trickled through. How he would like to leave it! The jungle half-light weighs down his spirits. He is tired of being always afraid.

The sunny plain beckons him, but he doesn't have the courage to leave the familiar for the unknown. He doesn't dare. And then one day fire thrusts him out. He runs, runs to the now familiar stream where he has caught so many fish. He splashes across to the other side, and his family trail behind.

After that break he turns back only once. When the flaming terror has died down, he goes back to the blackened jungle and picks up a burning stick. It is all he will take with him to the new adventure. With it he will go on and on. He will not turn back again.

For he is Man. Deep within him there is something that drives him, there is an urge he has to obey. "Go on!" it says to him. "Seek new places!"

Perhaps the new places will be worse than the old. Perhaps there will be more hunger, danger, cold. He doesn't know, he doesn't want to think about it. All he knows is he must go on.

There are deer in the open plain and herds of strange, swift-running creatures for which he has no name as yet. He stares at them curiously. He is glad when he sees them eating grass—that means they won't eat him. But time and again he sees the saber-tooth, too. Shelter must be found.

Now he has reached the hills and is scanning the heights for a hole of some kind to creep into. Up there in the wall of stone he thinks he sees one. It looks to be just a cleft in the solid rock, but when he clambers up he sees it is the opening to a wonderfully roomy cave. What is more, the cave is empty! Hyenas have lived here, but they are gone now. Perhaps they will come back?

He looks the entrance over. With stones and brush he can block it up so that no beast or marauding creature of his own kind can get in. Of his own kind, yes. He is afraid of his own kind even more than of the meat-eating beasts. For in the jungle he has learned that Man is the trickiest enemy of all. He will creep up on you sleeping and with a blow of club or stone smash in your head. He knows because he does the same thing. He hunts Man as Man hunts him. He likes the taste of human flesh. It is meat like any other—and more easily got.

The hungry children have run out to pick some hackberries they have seen near by. But the man and his wife busy themselves with the entrance. The woman struggles and pants over the heavy stones. For she isn't very big—only about four feet eight inches tall. And she isn't very strong and is quite unused to work. What work is there in the jungle to do? For that matter, her man is clumsy, too. He is a few inches taller, but he isn't so very much stronger. In the jungle he hasn't done very much to exercise his muscles. From now on he will have plenty of exercise, he sees. Here there are no trees to shelter him from his enemies—he will have to run, run fast to get away.

There, it is done. The shelter is safe, or almost safe. They have left just room enough at the entrance to get in and out by—at night they will block that, too, or else build a fire to frighten beasts. The woman goes to pick hackberries now. But the man climbs to the top of the hill. He wants to look down over the plain.

What an exciting place it is! There is a little stream with trees beside it, the rest is open and dry. Deer and fawns are drinking at the stream. The man looks at them hungrily. He cannot kill a deer. Not yet. He has no weapons that will kill from a distance. Nor has he learned to make a pitfall yet. That will come soon, but right now he has to depend on other killers—on the saber-tooth, the leopard, the wolf. Though they kill for themselves, they kill more than they can eat. Surely, he thinks, at dawn he will hear the death cry of the deer. The hyena will steal from the saber-tooth, and he will steal from the hyena.

A long time he stands there looking down. Then he, too, goes to eat hackberries. The cherry-like fruit isn't very filling. But he doesn't complain—he bears hunger well, he has learned to wait. In his imagination he sees a deer lying with its throat torn, blood gushing from the wound. It makes his mouth water. When he sees a sharp piece of quartz, he picks it up and takes it into the cave. He will need it to cut up the flesh when the saber-tooth and hyena have finished with the kill.

9. Man Against Mammoth

I̲ₜ ᴡᴀsɴ'ᴛ ᴀ ᴘʀᴇᴛᴛʏ ᴘɪᴄᴛᴜʀᴇ ᴏꜰ ᴍᴀɴ ᴛʜᴀᴛ ᴛʜᴇ
scientists got from the cave of Chou Kou Tien. But
they had to tell the truth. Some of them felt strongly
that *Sinanthropus* had been a cannibal. For the human leg bones in the cave were all cracked, the
skulls smashed. Should not the conclusion be drawn
that the long bones had been cracked for the marrow and the skulls smashed for the brains?

"In fact," one of the scientists said, "I am not
at all sure that *Sinanthropus* feasted only on his
enemies. It may even be that he ate his own children—or his wife when she didn't please him."

People turned in horror from an ancestor like that

—a man whose hand was against every other human being. They had rejected Neanderthal Man, thinking he was too dreadful a creature to be their ancestor. Why, Neanderthal Man was a gentleman and a scholar compared to Peking Man!

The more they learned about *Sinanthropus*, the less they thought of him. And the more they learned of Neanderthal Man, the more their respect for him grew. He was an ancestor to be proud of. He wasn't handsome, no. With those bone ridges jutting out over his eyes, that low, sloping forehead, the receding chin, the big head, barrel chest, short legs, long arms, big hands and feet, he wasn't handsome. But handsome is as handsome does. Think of a fellow no more than five feet four inches tall managing to live in the bitter cold of the Ice Age for a hundred thousand years or so! Think of a little fellow like that daring to hunt the mighty mammoth!

When in 1901 a frozen mammoth was found up in Siberia and people actually saw the monstrous beast Neanderthal Man had hunted, their respect for him shot 'way up. Why, the mammoth was a creature it would be hard to kill with a high-power rifle! And what did Neanderthal Man have? Stones!

Quite a fuss was made about the mammoth. He brought the Ice Age home to people. Here was actually one of the huge creatures that had walked about on top of the glacier. Here was one of the creatures along with whose bones people had been finding the tools and weapons of Neanderthal Man. And this mammoth wasn't just dry bones. He was flesh, blood, hide, everything. It was himself just as he was when, who knows how many thousands of years ago, he fell into a snow-covered crack in the glacier and got buried in the drifts.

The Russian scientists were thrilled when they got word that an elephant's head and foreleg were sticking out of the frozen earth in Siberia. They guessed at once it was an Ice Age mammoth, miraculously preserved. Of course, he was priceless. They went right up to get him out and put him in a museum.

And what a job they had! The part of him that was sticking out of the earth had started to decay, and the smell was so horrible they could hardly stand to come near. In fact, it was the smell that had led to the discovery. All the dogs for miles around had come to wrangle over the elephant meat, and their barking had brought people.

The scientists thought they'd have to give up. But they wanted the creature so much they forced themselves to stick it out. They dug and tugged and hauled—and finally they had him.

Well, what was he like?

In shape they saw he wasn't so very different from the elephants they knew except that his ears were small and just back of his neck he had a big hump of fat. Also his body sloped sharply down to his stumpy little tail. But he was covered all over with a yellowish woolly fur. On top of the fur he had a bristly coat of long hair, rusty brown in color. Some of it was fourteen inches long. His head had a mass of this long hair covering it like a cap. Patches of it also stood out like a mane on his cheeks and chin, shoulders and sides and belly.

"No wonder this fellow could keep warm in the Ice Age," the scientists thought.

But when they came to skinning him, they saw that he had something besides two coats to depend on. Under his skin was a layer of fat four inches thick!

The scientists cut through the frozen flesh and took out the stomach. Part of the mammoth's last meal was still in it—twenty-seven pounds of food that he hadn't digested. There were fir cones and bits of larch and fir and pine. There was sedge and wild thyme and two kinds of moss. And several hardy flowers. They could get quite an idea of what Neanderthal Man's scenery was like from that.

How had the little fellow managed to survive in that bitter cold time when only the hardiest plants could live? The mammoth was built for stormy weather. But Man had only his skin and a few little hairs here and there to protect him.

Yes, the frozen mammoth definitely made people's respect for Neanderthal Man go up. So did another discovery—only more.

Outside the village of La Chapelle-aux-Saints in southern France there was a cave in the side of a little hill. In the year 1905 three priests decided to try digging there. The cave, which was shallow—not more than five feet high at the highest point—was filled almost to the top with dirt. Wasn't it possible, they thought, that Neanderthal Man was responsible for some of that dirt?

Their hunch proved a good one. When after three years of digging and scraping and sifting they had examined all the dirt and got down to the floor of the cavern, they had a nice little collection of Neanderthal Man's flint tools and a great many bones of the animals he had killed and eaten.

But a much bigger prize was in store.

The three priests were almost through now. All that remained was to examine the hard, whitish floor. They were doing this for the last time when one of them exclaimed excitedly, "There seems to be a break here!"

He threw his light on the spot. The others did, too. In amazement they passed their hands over the place again and again.

It was clear that a hole had been dug here and afterwards filled in. Neanderthal Man must have done it. But what would he have dug the hole for? To bury someone! Under their feet must lie the bones of a human being—of Neanderthal Man!

Feverishly they started to dig away the soil, and in a little while they knew their guess was right. A skeleton lay before them. They were looking at the oldest burial in all the world.

The skeleton lay on its back, the head to the west, the left arm stretched out, the right one bent so that the hand lay near the head. Both legs were partly bent. Around the head a row of stones had been set, while around the body lay many worked flints. Food for the dead had been provided, too. Around the skeleton lay several large, flat pieces of the long bones of animals whose marrow Stone Age Man had so loved. Right by the head were the foot bones of a great ox or bison.

The three priests carefully examined the skeleton. They could tell that it was a man's and thought he was perhaps about fifty or fifty-five. He was short and had not stood quite upright. His great face was so beast-like that it sent a shudder through them. The lower part stuck out in a sort of muzzle, and over the large, deep eye sockets were enormous brow-ridges.

For a long time the three men silently gazed at the ugly features of the unknown. Who could tell what this man so different from themselves had been or done? One thing, however, the priests were sure of. He might have looked like a beast, but the thoughts that went on in his head had been such as no animal could have. This man and those who had laid him to rest so honorably had risen far above the beast. They had imagination, their thoughts had wings. Like the ancient Egyptians, like the Indians, like the priests themselves, they had believed in a spirit life beyond the grave. That was the meaning of the food and the tools. This man's friends had not wanted him to go to the strange new life empty-handed.

When news of the wonderful man of La Chapelle-aux-Saints came out in the papers, everybody buzzed about him, scientists and ordinary people, too. Well, they certainly had never suspected Neanderthal Man of that! A good hunter, yes. A fellow who could take the cold, yes. But a man who had looked beyond this life to the next—that was a surprise.

It brought Neanderthal Man close somehow. Before that common bond the thousands of years melted away. People saw him as though he had lived just yesterday.

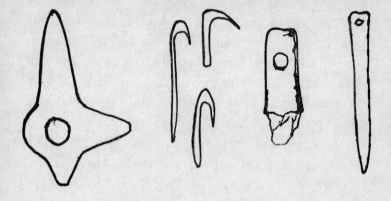

10. King of the Ice Age

It must have been around a hundred and thirty
thousand years ago when Neanderthal Man moved
into Europe.

"But why should anybody have wanted to go live
in Arctic cold?" people wondered. "If Neanderthal
Man wasn't satisfied where he was, why didn't he go
some place where it was warm?"

"That's just what he did do," the scientists told
them. "When he first got to Europe, it wasn't cold
there. It was warmer than it is today. That was a
time between glaciers. Three times the glacier had

come and three times it had melted away. Now it was so warm that hippopotami wallowed in the streams. Elephants with straight tusks, bison, wild horses, and cattle grazed in the meadows. The climate was fine and the hunting excellent.

"Just the same," the scientists went on in a puzzled sort of way, "we really can't say why he came. He was perfectly well off in the East. In those days the animals he hunted were so many and the creatures of his own kind were so few that he had plenty to eat right where he was."

No. There was no special reason for his coming. No practical reason, certainly. He wasn't driven by enemies, he wasn't driven by hunger. It was something else that pushed him, something deep inside him, something for which he had no name. He was restless. He wanted to be on the move, to be somewhere else than where he was. What lies beyond the plains? What's on the other side of the hills? He could go and satisfy his curiosity and still be sure he would have plenty to eat.

He loved to roam, he loved the open. He wasn't afraid of it the way his ancestors long ago had been.

For he is no longer Man with his hand raised against every other man. He is no longer Man who takes the leavings of the hyena as the hyena takes what the saber-tooth has left. He is a big game hunter—and he doesn't hunt alone. The creatures he hunts are so big that he has to join with others of his own kind if he wants to live well. So he has companions besides his wife and children. He has friends now. And when a man is out in the open with his friends to stand by him, he isn't afraid.

There is something else that gives him courage—he has a weapon now. He has learned to make tools out of flint, and with those tools he can make a spear. He smooths and sharpens a long stick to a point, hardens it in the fire, and there's his weapon ready. It will go through any hide he knows. Sometimes he lashes a flint point onto his wooden spear and makes it better still.

Flint! What a wonderful stone it is! Flint doesn't have to be struck off a big rock. He can find it in chunks of the right size in the chalk of which there is so much here. And flint is hard, harder than anything in his world. At the same time it is brittle. He can take one of the shiny stones in his hand, strike the edge with another flint, and chips will fly off. He can strike off chips all around the edge and top, and the core will make a fine, heavy chopper or a digging stone that fits into his hand. Or he can use the core for a spear point.

But the chips he has struck off are even better, he

64

thinks, than the core. Out of them he can make any number of sharp-edged tools for cutting and piercing and scraping. His ancestors didn't care for the chips much—mostly they worked with the core. But he uses the core only for his heavy work and the chips for all the other things. There's nothing better for knife or scraper or borer than a large flake of flint.

How he prizes his tools! They are his very life— he can't kill without them. Any time he isn't hunting or sleeping or eating, he is squatting down chipping. He keeps his eye always on the lookout for new pieces of flint.

Even little ones are good—he can make fire with them. For now he has learned how. No longer does he have to light a new fire with a burning brand from some other fire as his ancestors did. He takes a piece of flint in his hand and strikes it with another piece of flint and lo! a hot spark flies off. He has dry moss or wood dust handy. The spark flies into it— and there's his fire. He can have one in a moment's time whenever he likes.

Europe is a happy hunting ground, and with his tools Neanderthal Man is king in it. What more could a man ask of life? He has a shelter of boughs to protect him, a deerskin to drape over his shoulders, a fire to cook the meat he brings home in plenty. He is content. For thousands of years he is master of all he looks upon.

But now little by little it begins to grow colder. The winter starts earlier and lasts longer. Heavy clouds everlastingly scud across the sky. You can't tell the difference from year to year. You can hardly tell it from century to century. But all the time through thousands of years the climate is changing for the worse. It is damp, damp, and getting damper; cold, colder, bitter cold.

Higher and higher the snowdrifts pile. They pack down and turn to ice. Up north the ice starts moving. For a fourth time the glaciers are coming down. Already the lands that one day will be called Scandinavia and Finland are under ice. Rivers of ice fill the valleys of Germany. In Scotland all the mountain valleys have glaciers in them. Arctic plants begin to grow along the Thames where one day London will stand. England is a bleak and almost treeless country now. All of Europe north of the Pyrenees is in the grip of Arctic cold.

Shelters of branches are no longer enough—Man needs better protection now. Shall he then leave this land which his fathers possessed before him? The Neanderthaler is not a fellow to run away. He is not very big, but he is no coward—he is used to standing his ground and fighting it out against the beasts. Shall he run from cold? Besides, what use will it be to go to some warmer place if he will find no flint there?

No. He will stay here where he knows he can find it, and get around the weather one way or another. The hunting is good again now. Though the warmth-loving animals are all gone, strange new creatures have moved down from the north.

Some families are lucky. They find a limestone cave and settle down in it. But there aren't many caves, and every time you spot one, it is sure to be occupied by fierce, furry lions or huge bears that will stand and fight to the death. Sometimes a dozen or more live in a single cave.

How to get rid of the beasts is the problem. But it must be solved because this terrible cold is getting to be more than they can bear.

They could try fire perhaps. Supposing all the hunters armed themselves with spears and clubs and stones and then built a smoky fire at the entrance to a cavern. If the wind was right, the smoke would blow inside. The beasts would have to get out or smother. The men would stand right by the entrance and slaughter the creatures as they came out coughing and blinded by the smoke. Then if afterwards the beasts came back, the family could frighten them away with fire.

No sooner thought than done. Oh, wonderful change! How good it is to squat with a shelter over your head and no fear of a beast behind you! It isn't warm in the cave, but it isn't so cold as outside. And you can always build a fire in the cavern entrance or on the terrace just outside and warm yourself.

When the weather is clear, the family like the terrace best. It's out on the terrace that the Neanderthaler does his cooking and his chipping. It's there that his wife scrapes the pelts to make them soft. She has a lot of scraping to do. Every time her man comes home his furs are wet and stiff. When they have dried off, she scrapes and scrapes them so the leather won't rub his skin. He is a good provider, this man of hers, and she does what she can to make him comfortable.

"The hunting is not what it was in the good old days," her husband's old father says, shaking his great head as he sits by the fire. "In my father's father's father's time they hunted the straight-tusked elephant and the hippopotamus."

The young Neanderthaler thinks the hunting isn't bad at all. But it is different. There's the mammoth now. You can't get near enough to strike with all your body's strength on account of that terrible trunk of his that can swing you up in the air and dash you senseless on the ground. Besides, you've found out that even all your body's force can't send a spear through that beast's hide. And he's too smart to be driven over a cliff. You've got to get together with other men and dig a deep pitfall for him. And when he's fallen in—how well you'll know it by his angry trumpeting!—you can run and throw great stones down on him.

Yes, the hunting is different. The mammoth and the woolly rhinoceros with his terrible double horn are hard to kill. You have to trap them or come at them when they're stuck in a bog.

The other creatures are easier to kill. You can drive the bison, the wild horses and cattle, the giant deer and reindeer over a cliff. Or you can bring them down with spears or throwing stones fastened to a leather thong. Once they are down, it is easy enough to finish them off with your knife.

Oh, the excitement when you have such a creature down! You strip off the pelt right where he lies. You cut off the thighs and the shoulders, you split the head for the brain. Then you take your favorite pieces home in the pelt to cook at the fire—on the terrace if the weather's good, in the cavern opening if it isn't.

69

II. Lartet Finds the Reindeer Men

A HUNDRED YEARS AGO THERE LIVED IN THE LITTLE village of Aurignac in southern France a farmer by the name of Bonnemaison. One crisp fall day he was out with his gun in the hills and had just spotted a fine rabbit. He was waiting impatiently to get a good shot at it when, to his annoyance, the creature bounded away up a slope and dived into a hole. Bonnemaison went right up after it.

"There's more than one way to get a rabbit," he thought. He put his hand into the hole, expecting to pull the animal out by its ears. To his surprise, his hand closed on something hard. It was a human bone!

What could it mean? Had somebody been murdered here?

Bonnemaison started digging the earth away fast. He could feel a large slab of stone underneath. It seemed to him, as he uncovered it, that it was blocking the entrance to what might be a cave. He pulled and he pushed and finally got the stone out.

His eyes almost started from his head when he saw a cave filled nearly to the top with human bones. He forgot all about his rabbit. Running down the slope, he hurried straight to the Mayor to tell him the ghastly news.

Now the Mayor of Aurignac was not a man to get excited. He was a practical fellow who did his duty and minded his own business. So he didn't ask, "Where are those bones?" Or "Who put them there?" He simply said, "We'll give them Christian burial," and went about getting it done. Seventeen skeletons of men, women, and children were taken out of the cave and quietly put away in the parish cemetery.

Eight years passed. It was now 1860. Everybody

in Aurignac had long ago forgotten about the bones
when one day a gentleman arrived and inquired
about them. It was Edouard Lartet, a French
lawyer, who, like Dr. Rigollot of Amiens, was trying
to help Boucher de Perthes get recognition for his
Stone Age Man.

"Where are the skeletons that came out of the
cave?" Lartet asked the Mayor. "I want to examine
them. They are important for science."

"For science!" The Mayor was flustered. "Alas!"
he exclaimed. "It was so long ago, Monsieur! They
are certainly somewhere in the parish cemetery, but
where exactly . . . who can say? However," he
added quickly as he saw the gentleman's face fall,
"you may rest assured, Monsieur, that the bones had
Christian burial."

Lartet saw it was hopeless—he couldn't very
well go digging among tombstones.

"Then I will study the cave," he said.

The Mayor at once arranged for a guide, and in
a short time Lartet found himself in the cave which
eight years ago only a rabbit had known. Doubt-
fully he regarded the deposit that lay many feet
thick on the cave floor. He had no idea as he took
his coat off, laid his watch carefully on it, and noted
the time that this was one of the great moments in
the story of Stone Age Man.

For out of that cave—and more especially out
of the sloping terrace that went up to it—his pick
was to bring to light tools and weapons such as no
one in France had ever seen before. There were
finely made objects of flint and bone and ivory
mixed in with the split long bones of cave-bear and
mammoth and rhinoceros and reindeer. There were
necklaces of sea shells and teeth pierced with holes
for stringing. There were bone pins and cleverly
made buttons.

Strangest of all were the many, many tools and
weapons made of reindeer antler. Clearly whoever
had made such things had lived at a time when reindeer were plentiful in France. And that was when?
Twenty thousand years ago or twenty-five? Whenever it was, anyone could see, Lartet thought, that
the Reindeer Men had lived in an Age Before Metals, in an age when stone and bone and ivory and
horn had been the great materials.

Lartet felt strangely moved as he took from the
terrace the barbed weapons, the bone pins, and the
buttons. He felt so privileged. How many people
had passed over this little piece of revealing earth
without ever guessing the treasures that lay under
the grasses and wild flowers! It had been given to
him to find this forgotten people of the Reindeer
Age—a people whose name he had to invent, whose

story he could only guess at, whose faces he couldn't even imagine.

Chance had led Edouard Lartet to discover the Reindeer Men. Chance so arranged things that his own son was the first to find out what they had looked like.

A railroad was being built in southern France in the year 1868. The work had got down as far as the village of Cro-Magnon. One day the men were busy working around a cliff when they accidentally broke into a rock shelter at its base. To their amazement they saw a heap of human bones inside—five skeletons lay on the shelter floor.

Now, skeletons are always news. So very soon the story was all around and before long had got to the ears of the Minister of Public Education. Fortunately this man had read all about the cave of Aurignac and how through ignorance the bones had been lost to science. Edouard Lartet, he knew, was too old to undertake the job of examining the Cro-Magnon shelter. Would his son Louis do it?

Louis Lartet was delighted to be asked. How many times he and his father had talked about the Reindeer Men and wondered what they had looked like! Now perhaps these five skeletons would prove to be the very ancestors they so longed to see.

With the greatest curiosity he hurried down to Cro-Magnon.

Two skeletons, he found, were of men, two of women, and the last was a tiny baby's. All had been buried, Lartet thought, at the same, or almost the same, time. And one, at least, of the five had been murdered; for there was an enormous hole in her forehead. Probably, he thought, she was the mother of the baby lying at her side.

But who were these mysterious people, all of whom perhaps had met with sudden and terrible death? The shelter itself must tell him that.

Carefully Louis Lartet carried the bones out and began to examine the floor. All was just as at Aurignac. The same hearths, the same mammoth and rhinoceros and cave-bear bones split for the marrow, the same tools and weapons of flint and bone and reindeer antler.

Lartet waited till he had been through every inch of the cave floor before he went back to the skeletons. Now that he was sure these were the Reindeer Men whose tools and weapons and ornaments his father had uncovered, he was astonished to see how much like people of his own day they were. He couldn't tell the difference except for the fact that the Reindeer Men were taller, better looking, and had bigger brains.

He couldn't take his eyes off one handsome old man's skull. It was in better condition than the others because it had lain where the drip of the cave had fallen on it and preserved it. The broad face, the high forehead, the eye sockets so broad and shallow, the narrow nose and prominent chin were strangely pleasing to him. What a wonderfully handsome race of people this had been! And how astonishing that Homo *sapiens*, modern Man, had lived in France so long ago.

Of course, he knew scientists and he knew what they would say. They wouldn't believe that an extinct race of people like themselves had lived in France at a time when reindeer found it comfortable there. They would say that these people belonged to a much later time and had dug up and used the antlers of reindeer that had died thousands of years before.

Let them argue. He knew it was impossible for the Reindeer Men to have lived only at Aurignac and Cro-Magnon. They must have lived in many caves of southern France. Time would bring to light more of these wonderfully skilled workers in stone and bone and reindeer horn. Time would prove him right.

12. Bulls on a Ceiling

"Now that's something like!" people said when it was finally settled that Cro-Magnon Man and the reindeer had lived in France together. Everybody liked the idea of having tall, handsome, brainy ancestors who so many thousands of years ago had swept like conquerors into Europe. In fact, people couldn't give them credit enough.

"Look at these barbed weapons and pins and pendants and beads and buttons made by Cro-Magnon Man," people would exclaim. "What a skilled worker he was!"

Cro-Magnon Man got quite a display at the International Exhibition in Paris. But still the credit he got wasn't nearly as much as he deserved. Chance had brought a lot of his work to light. Now it was about to disclose something so extraordinary that people wouldn't believe it was his.

In the same year that Louis Lartet first looked upon the Reindeer Men, a sportsman went hunting on a farm in Spain. He had his dog with him. The animal was doing a little hunting on his own and had chased somewhere out of sight when suddenly the hunter heard him whining.

He found the animal caught in some rocks fallen from the hillside. Before the sportsman could get him out, he had to move quite a few large chunks of stone. Afterwards he noticed how all unknowingly he had opened the entrance to a cave.

He stepped in and took a look around. It was cool and silent and dark inside. Deep shadows filled all but the part near the entrance, yet there was light enough for the hunter to see that the whole floor was cluttered with fallen rock. Awed by the mystery of the place, he stood there a moment, then stepped

out into the light. It never occurred to him that this
cave had been the home of Cro-Magnon Man—he
knew nothing about such things.

Now Spain is a country in which poor people will
often make their home in a cave for want of a
better place. But this particular cave on "Altamira"
farm was so choked with stone that even the poorest
peasant didn't want to move into it. So nobody disturbed what Cro-Magnon Man had left behind him
until a Spanish nobleman from the town of Santan-
der near by decided to explore the cave.

Don Marcellino de Sautuola had just been to
the International Exhibition and had been much
excited by the wonderful things that had come out
of the French caves. "Perhaps," he thought, "the
caves of Spain hold such things, too." Accordingly,
the minute he got back he made arrangements to
dig in the cave of Altamira.

One day he brought along his little daughter
Maria. Don Marcellino gave her a candle like his
own, and telling her to be careful, went about his
digging. But casting shadows on the walls didn't
amuse Maria very long. She squeezed herself in here
and wormed herself in there, and suddenly found
herself in another chamber, to the left and behind
the entrance hall. Raising her candle high, she
looked around the walls, then up at the ceiling. Her

heart almost stopped beating. Fierce eyes were staring at her from above!

"Bulls!" the terrified little girl shrieked.

Her father came stumbling over the rocks to her side. He held his candle up where the child pointed. There on the ceiling was the most amazing sight the cave explorer had ever seen. His knees almost gave as he looked at it.

Painted in glorious colors of red, yellow, brown, violet, black, and white was a herd of eighteen bison. They stood and lay in every imaginable position. Some were quietly standing, some were furiously bounding forward. Others, again, were advancing with lazy motion. Some were curled up in sleep. The great beasts looked so real that Don Marcellino didn't wonder his little girl was terrified. He himself had the strangest feeling as he stared back into the eyes that glared down on him.

He reached up to the low vault and passed his hand over a painted flank. The colors were as fresh as though they had been put on yesterday. How had the marvelous work been done? This chamber was so far from the cave entrance that the light of day had never entered it. By what light had the artist worked?

De Sautuola examined the walls. There wasn't a

trace of soot on them. A lamp, then, must have been used.

And what about the paints? Vegetable carbon and ocher would have given the artist red and yellow and brown. But where did he get the violet?

De Sautuola stared and stared. The work was so wonderful it would do credit to any artist of his own day. In fact, it looked surprisingly modern. Nothing like it had been found in the French caves. Nothing like this had even been suspected. Art like this just didn't go with people who strung teeth and sea shells into necklaces.

For surely this *was* the work of Cro-Magnon Man. Whoever made these paintings must have seen and studied the living beasts. In no other way could he have got all the little details that made the creatures look so positively alive. And bison had died out in Spain at the end of the Ice Age.

De Sautuola was in a fever about his find, yet he felt it wouldn't be wise to tell anyone about it. First he must finish exploring the floor. "But when I do reveal my secret," he thought, "what a stir it will make!"

To his amazement there was no stir at all—scientists simply refused to believe in the paintings. What? Superb paintings by Cro-Magnon Man? Su-

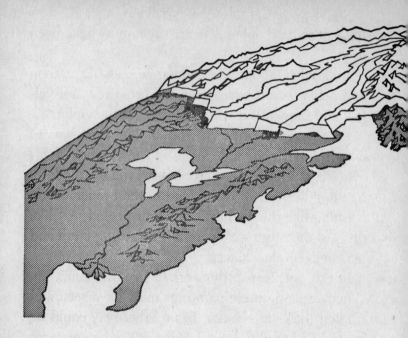

perb art by somebody who wore animal teeth around his neck and lived thousands of years before the Egyptians? Nonsense. Art didn't start out that way. It had childish beginnings, it grew up over thousands of years. Some trickster had gone into the cave and put the paintings there to fool De Sautuola. Didn't he himself say the colors looked as fresh as though put on yesterday? How could paint have stayed so bright for—say—fifteen or twenty thousand years?

In vain Don Marcellino pointed out how unlikely

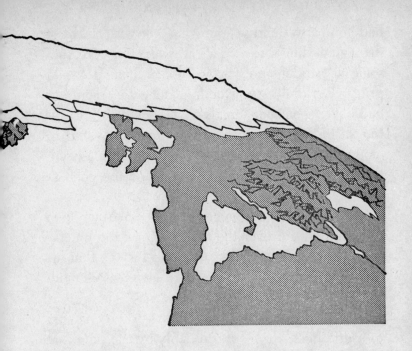

it was that an artist would play such a joke on him. "Would anyone ever put the paintings on the ceiling of a pitch-dark room where there was every chance I would never find them?" he said. "It makes no sense."

But except for one solitary professor from the University of Madrid, nobody would bother to go and see the paintings. He alone helped De Sautuola defend the bison.

But as time went on, the two men found they were talking to deafer and deafer ears. For an artist had gone into the cave and come out with the most damaging things to say about the bison. He said some art student must have copied them from old prints. Certainly whoever had done the paintings had never seen the animals alive—the drawing was too distorted. The forger had doubtless studied modern art but hadn't learned very much. In a word, the bison were too bad to be real and too good to be old.

"Too bad and too good. . . ." Don Marcellino grew thoughtful over the report. "I ask too much," he said to himself. "I ask people to believe that art was rich, wonderful, and modern at its very beginning. It upsets the whole theory."

Well, the theory would just have to be changed to fit the facts, that's all. Probably by the time that happened he would be dead. But the paintings would live on—the time would come when Cro-Magnon Man would get the credit he deserved. Having waited so many thousands of years, the old fellow could afford to wait a little longer.

13. Is It a Forgery?

IF CHANCE HAD NOT COME TO HIS RESCUE, IT MIGHT indeed have taken a very long time for Cro-Magnon Man to come into his own. But Chance, that had already done so much for him, was prepared to do much more.

In the village of La Mouthe in southern France there lived a farmer who made use of everything that came to hand. There was a cave on his place.

He made use of that. He cleaned out the dirt and the bones and the teeth that were in it and threw them on his fields for fertilizer. He built a wall of stones across the entrance, set a door in the middle, and there was a barn ready-made—a fine place to store his beets and potatoes.

For fifty years the farmer did this. Then one day a doctor arrived at the farm. Could he explore the "barn"? He was studying the caves of southern France, he said, and here was one that had never been explored.

Of course, as soon as Emile Rivière saw how clean the "barn" was, he realized it was no use searching the front part—there was nothing left to find. If anything of real value was to come out of the cave, it would have to come from the deep interior.

So he tried his pick in the most distant part of the cave. And in a few minutes he had the information he wanted. Here were reindeer teeth, bison bones, finely worked flints, and a shell pierced with a hole. To his experienced eyes these things meant Cro-Magnon Man. Rivière at once came to terms with the farmer, making it clear that the old man was to leave everything strictly alone till he, Rivière, came back to search the place thoroughly.

However, the farmer just couldn't keep out of

his "barn." An urge to level the floor all at once
seized him. Thinking he could get it done before
the doctor came back, he dug away against time.
But his plan fell through. He was hard at work one
morning when part of the rear wall suddenly gave
way, revealing a hole where the wall had been.

The farmer looked at it in amazement. It was
a narrow, half-moon-shaped opening that looked
just like an oven. He put his arm inside and felt
around. He couldn't feel any end to the hole. He
had always thought the cave ended at the rear wall,
but evidently here was a passage that led deep into
the hill!

When a few days later Emile Rivière returned
with a couple of men and saw the hole, he didn't
have any reproaches to make. He was too excited.
Where did the hole lead? Everybody wanted to find
out at once; so one after another the three men
crawled in.

Holding their lanterns in front of them, they
advanced slowly on all fours through the narrow,
clay-filled corridor—eighty, ninety, a hundred yards.
Suddenly Rivière, who was in the lead, uttered a
sharp cry and threw his light up. The others hurried
to catch up with him, threw their lights upward as
he was doing—and caught their breath. They stared
unbelieving. The walls and ceiling of the corridor

were covered with magnificent engravings of animals—bison, ibex, reindeer, wild horse!

Trembling with excitement, the men crawled on for thirty-five yards more, past one creature of a bygone age after another. Then the pictures ended. The explorers followed the passage for another hundred yards. But there strong columns of stalactites blocked the passage and forced them to return.

When the three men came out of the cave and stood once more in the sunlight, they could hardly believe they had seen what they had seen. It seemed so fantastic. For a little while nobody wanted to speak—they felt as though they had just returned from another world. Then one of the men said, "How ever did they make those engravings in that narrow space?"

"It wasn't always that narrow," Rivière answered thoughtfully. "The clay that chokes the corridor wasn't there when the engravings were made. You noticed that the lower limbs of the animals were hidden by the clay. What can it mean but that it was washed into the corridor afterwards?"

"But why do you suppose Cro-Magnon Man put the engravings in a place that must always have been pitch dark? Why didn't he put them on the walls of a chamber people lived in, where everybody could see them?"

Rivière shrugged his shoulders. He couldn't answer. The same question had been running through his own mind.

It haunted him all through the weeks he crouched in the corridor copying the engravings. He remembered that in the cave of Altamira the animal pictures had also been put in a distant, dark chamber. What meaning was there in that?

He couldn't solve the riddle. When with a sketchbook filled with the art work of Cro-Magnon Man he arrived at the Academy of Sciences, he still had not solved it.

One by one he passed the astonishing bison, ibex, reindeer, and wild horse around. The bearded scientists looked and looked at them. But they said nothing.

Rivière grew impatient. "Well?" he finally said.

"The engravings are too beautiful to be the work of Cro-Magnon Man," one old gentleman remarked. "They are too well done to have been made so long ago."

Others took up the cry. "Yes, yes, they are too beautiful! They are too well done!"

"It is a forgery," the old gentleman continued. "Someone put the engravings there after the corridor was opened up and before Monsieur Rivière explored it."

Rivière was upset. "Who could have done the work in that narrow space where one can't stand up?" he protested. "Who would have taken the trouble first to make the engravings and then to fill the passage in with clay in such a way as to hide the lower limbs of the beasts? Besides, if the engravings were just made, wouldn't they differ in color from the neighboring rock? And the color is the same!"

It was no use. Just as the scientists had refused to believe in the Altamira paintings, so now they refused to believe in the engravings.

But time had marched on. After the meeting was over, one by one and two by two the doubters rode out to La Mouthe to see the engravings for themselves. And one by one and two by two they came away convinced.

With what shame they now recalled the silly things they had said about the bison in the cave of Altamira!

"We made a bad mistake that time," the most learned of the scientists declared at their next meeting. "Now I for one am ready to confess publicly how wrong I have been. Gentlemen, we must let all the world know how great an artist Cro-Magnon Man was."

14. Bison of Clay

PEOPLE WERE QUITE WILLING TO HEAR THAT THEIR pet ancestor was a skilled painter and etcher. When a few years later scientists announced that on top of everything else Cro-Magnon Man was a sculptor, everybody was delighted to hear that, too. They were all the more delighted as the story Max Begouen told was like something out of the *Arabian Nights.*

On the estate of his father, the Count Begouen, just north of the Pyrenees Mountains in France, there was a natural wonder—a rivulet flowed out from under a mountain. What was this little river? Max and his two brothers and his father puzzled a great deal over it. They knew that not far from this spot two streams mysteriously disappeared into a mountain. Did these two perhaps join under the ground and come out together?

There was but one way to find out. That was to enter the Tuc d'Audoubert, as the underground tunnel was called, and see what happened to the stream. So in the summer of 1912, Max, Jacques, and Louis built themselves a little boat and pushed off into the blackness of the mountain.

Slowly, cautiously they moved forward. Only their acetylene lamps broke the midnight darkness of the tunnel. Yellow limestone arched in a dome over their heads, yellow limestone walls shut them in on either side. There seemed to be no break anywhere. Two hundred yards upstream, however, they caught sight of an opening in the wall. If that was a passage, where did it lead?

Mooring their boat on a little clay beach, the brothers made for the break. And now they saw that, all unknown to the outside world, a magnificent cavern slept in the heart of the mountain. Chamber after mysterious chamber opened before them. They followed inclines up and inclines down. They clambered over impossible rocks to galleries on another level. And suddenly with a shock they realized they weren't the first to enter here.

For standing out sharp and clear on one wall was the outline of a horse. It was a little wild horse with thick, upstanding mane. Its ears were erect, its nose thrust forward, and in its side was a deeply cut dart. Near by on another wall a second horse caught their eye, then a bison, then the head of a reindeer with huge antlers. Between its eye and ear the boys noticed a curious downward slash. Was that meant for a club?

"Whoever made those pictures never got in the way we did," Max, who was the eldest, remarked. "The water's low now. If it rose even a little, they would have run the risk of getting trapped. There must have been another entrance."

"Well, we aren't going to look for it now, Max," Jacques said. "Let's go ahead and explore the rest of the cave!"

The river was forgotten. That day, and day after day in the weeks that followed, the boys explored. Often the Count, their father, came with them. Sometimes their valet, François Camel, came along to help.

One day—it was early in October, about three months after they began exploring—François and the boys were alone in the cave. Max was copying some engravings from a wall in the upper galleries. Jacques and Louis were exploring near by, while the valet poked about at the far end of the chamber. They all believed this little low-ceilinged room was the last in the gallery. But suddenly François, who had been playing his light around among the stalagmites, cried out, "There's another chamber beyond!"

The boys all dropped what they were doing and rushed over to see. There *was* a room beyond. Pounding away excitedly with whatever first came to hand, they broke a cat-hole through the pillars that blocked their way and in a little while could wriggle through. Curiously they played their lights on the chamber walled off thousands of years ago.

The first thing they saw was a bear's skull. Beyond it they could make out a skeleton—and another and another. The skeletons lay all over the chamber, just where the fierce creatures had dropped down ages ago to die. Max and François picked up the nearest skull and opened the great jaws. At once both noticed the same thing—the bear's eye-teeth were missing. They were missing in the next skull and the next!

"They were pulled out!" Max exclaimed with conviction. "See! Here are the marks of a man's

94

knees deep in the floor where I'm standing. Look how he struggled to force the teeth from the jaws! For necklaces, of course."

"Before ever the men came," François said solemnly, "the bears lived and died here." The sense of how long ago it all was made his voice husky.

But Jacques and Louis had already gone on. They had seen that the chamber of the bears was only the first of a whole new set of rooms and galleries and were quickly passing from one to another. Max and François hurried to catch up.

A strange, almost religious feeling uplifted the four as they passed from one pure-white chamber to the next. So, all unknowing, they advanced to the great adventure. . . .

In all the chambers they passed through, they had seen no sign of engravings on the walls. But now again animals began to appear above them. Thrilled by the new find, the explorers were moving on to the last chamber when Max, who was in the rear, let out a cry of astonishment that made the others turn. By chance his lamp had lit up a great stone block at his feet. And on this block was something so amazing that he stood staring speechless. Two statues of bison, two statues modeled out of clay, stood on the block as if set up on an altar. One of the bison was male, the other was a female. Each was about a yard long. The cow was leading, the bull followed close behind.

They looked alive. The two bison were modeled so wonderfully, they had such a modern look about them that it was hard to believe they were perhaps the oldest statues in the world. The explorers stood around them as though riveted. Only Jacques could bear to tear his eyes away.

"Look here, fellows!" they heard him say.

In the clay of the floor another bison was deeply outlined. The sculptor had just begun to work on it, had just got to the point of lifting it out of the clay to mold like the others. Was it to have been part of the same group? "Why didn't he come back to finish it?" flashed through all their minds.

Max reached out now and gently touched one of the statues. The clay was still moist and soft. Along the neck where the sculptor had modeled the hair, the marks of the artist's hand clearly showed. The marks of his bare feet pressed down the floor all around the bison. And when the boys stepped into the little chamber next door, where the sculptor had gone for clay, they could see the marks of his heels there, right where he had squatted to dig.

It just didn't seem possible that perhaps fifteen thousand years had passed since those prints were made. The marks in the floor looked as though the artist had stood there yesterday.

What had he made the bison for? Surely not to decorate the chamber. For no one had lived in this pitch-dark part of the cavern in the depths of the mountain. No one had even entered the room after the artist had got this far in his work—no marks of feet disturbed his own footsteps.

Why had he never returned to finish his work?

"Maybe," Max suggested, "he couldn't get back into the cave. Maybe a landslide sealed off the entrance. Maybe that's the reason we've never found out where it was."

15. End of a Hero

HE WASN'T ALWAYS A SCULPTOR. HE WASN'T ALWAYS
a painter and engraver. When you first see him, his
hands are skilled only in chipping flint and carving
bone and horn and ivory. Cro-Magnon Man is too
busy moving around to do much else. He follows the
game. He is here, he is there, he is forever on the
move.

For countless centuries, for thousands upon thousands of years he has been trekking. He has walked all the way from Asia—and he couldn't tell you why. "I follow the game," he would say, but that wouldn't be the real reason.

He doesn't know the real reason. He can't explain the gnawing restlessness that stirs inside him, that urges, that pushes, that drives him on. Like Neanderthal Man before him—in those long-ago days before the little fellow took to the caves—he wants to go on. He wants to be somewhere else than where he is. His eyes must rest on new places. What is on that other side of the dark, forested hills? What lies beyond this sheltered valley? Where does the swollen torrent empty its icy waters?

He is a wanderer, an explorer—and a very mighty hunter. Time was when Man ran from the beasts. Now the beasts run from Man. They cannot endure the smell of this hairless, two-legged creature. This being without horns, without claws, without tusks is more to be feared than the lion. Always he has new and newer ways of killing them. Now there's the barbed bone harpoon that goes jaggedly into the flesh. An animal can get rid of the stick to which the harpoon head is fixed if he strikes against tree or bush or if he rolls upon the ground. But the barbed head sticks deep and holds. He can't get rid of that.

Cro-Magnon Man follows the game. But when

you first see him, his wanderings are almost over.
He himself doesn't know it. He doesn't guess that
this fair land he has discovered is land's end for him
—or almost. He has no inkling that here among the
limestone cliffs of a country that will one day be
called France he is at last going to settle down. For
fifteen thousand years he is going to stay.

These sheltered valleys teem with beasts. And
he has come to them in the pleasant summertime,
when the willows and birches are green. The terrible
cold that the old folks still talk about is over now.
The glaciers have retreated to the mountains. To be
sure, so much water is still locked in them that the
level of the ocean is down. You could walk from
Africa to Europe across the land bridges. Or from
France to England—there is no English Channel
between. There is no channel between England and
Ireland. The British Isles are all part of the Continent. And the Baltic Sea is a great fresh-water lake.

Yes, the glaciers have retreated to the mountains.
Still, even in summer the rushing rivers they feed
are ice-cold. The air is cold even in summer. But
this newcomer has known only arctic cold for thousands of years now—he doesn't mind it. He likes
this green and sunny land. He likes the dark forests
of spruce and fir that line the slopes of the valleys.
Moss is plentiful for the reindeer that he sees wan-

dering about in great herds. The mammoth, the woolly rhinoceros, and the musk-ox all make good eating.

There is the best of hunting here, the best—and he soon learns he isn't the only one that knows it. There is a race of little men here who hunt with flint-tipped wooden spears. The men have heavy heads with beetling brows. Their hands and feet are big and their short legs never quite straighten out. He can see them lighting their evening fires on the narrow terraces in front of their shelters.

Yes, even in summer these strange folk live in caves. Cro-Magnon Man wonders at that. It is only when the white drifts pile up against the rocks and tree trunks that he starts thinking of a shelter. Well, here there will be no lack of that. Those little stunted hunters won't be very hard to drive from their holes.

And the day comes. Oh, fearful day for the little Neanderthaler! Long ago—remember with what courage!—he drove out the fierce cave-bear and the lion. Now like another beast he is himself driven from his home. But in this bitter climate to lose your shelter is to die. So he stands and fights, fights for the last time—and goes down fighting.

Are there cheers for the hero as he falls? Alas! These fair-skinned, handsome invaders have no sense of kinship with him. They just throw his body out. They take over his shelter. They don't know that for a hundred thousand years the little fellow has been king of Europe. They don't know he stuck it out through the bitterest cold of the Ice Age. Out he goes!

His wife, now, that's another matter. Let her stay. She will scrape the pelts and tend to the fires. Let her stay. Let her be someone's wife who has no woman of his own.

16. Midnight Magic in a Cave

CRO-MAGNON MAN HAS TAKEN TO THE CAVES THE
year around now. Even in summer he thinks the
open is too cold. But back in a land he passed
through thousands of years ago, in a land that someday will be called Czechoslovakia, his cousins the
Mammoth Hunters still camp in the open, comes
summer.

There is a sheltered valley here that breaks
through a half circle of hills. It is the valley of the

Becva River. Someday the railway from Warsaw to
Vienna will run through this valley. But now it is
a highway for the mammoth in his thousands. It is
a highway for horse and reindeer—and for the lion
that preys on them. For this is the gateway to the
flat plains of Poland and Silesia. It is by way of the
valley that the creatures go to the grasslands. And
here right in their path the Mammoth Hunters have
set up their camp.

Bitter cold are the winters in these closing years
of the Ice Age. The snows pile high. The cutting
winds are cruel. You hug the fire under your rock
shelter or in front of your cave. You wait longingly
for summer. And when it comes it is so brief. You
barely have time to thaw out before the snow starts
falling again. But oh, it is a good time, summer. Summer is the time of labor and fullness and excitement
and rejoicing. It is the time of feasts.

You pitch your tent in the open valley, in the row
with all the other tents, facing the great hearths.
Then you get out your digging tools. You have to
dig pits for the mammoths along their trails. Then
you get the great pear-shaped mammoth stones
ready. You have to wrap them up tightly in hide.
Afterwards you tie a long thong around the narrow
end. You drop the stone on the mammoth's head,
haul up and drop again.

It takes a lot to kill a mammoth, but you are not called Mammoth Hunter for nothing. There in the refuse pits behind the tents lie the bones of a hundred thousand mammoths. You and your fathers before you and their fathers 'way back have helped to pile those bones. There they are, neat as winter cordwood. Three huge piles of mammoth tusks with a little path between the piles. A huge pile of thigh bones—you put them in the fire and the fat oozes out and keeps the flame bright. An enormous field of mammoth hip bones, just hip bones, nothing else. And another one of lower jaws.

They are mighty hunters, these mammoth eaters. But all the cousins of Cro-Magnon Man are mighty hunters. Not so far away from him in France, at a place that will be called Solutré someday, they hunt the horse. The bones of a hundred thousand horses lie around that camp.

These eaters of horse flesh do more than hunt. They are skilled workers in flint. Nobody in the world can make such slender, beautiful knives as theirs. They are a foot long and chipped so thin you can almost see through them.

The Solutreans work horse bone, too. They've hit on a wonderful new invention. They take a very narrow, sharp bone splinter and shape it smooth into an awl. Then in the wider part at the top they drill a hole. It looks like an eye. You put a well-dried tendon through the hole and see! The tendon follows the awl in and out wherever you push it. It makes stitches. You can sew two pieces of softened hide together like that. The invention is so wonderful that their cousin at Cro-Magnon has started copying it. The women think there's nothing like a needle when it comes to making clothes.

Yes, Cro-Magnon Man is learning. He borrows from his cousins whatever he can. But he is no mere borrower. He makes fishhooks and daggers of bone. He makes drills and saws. He sews ivory buttons on his clothes. He carves artificial shells and teeth out of ivory.

And he invents the atlatl. That's a spear thrower. It is a rod into which you fit the spear shaft. You hold the atlatl in your throwing hand and you cast. The spear flies off, but the spear thrower stays in your hand. The spear goes farther and flies faster because of the atlatl. It is just as though your arm was longer and could throw farther.

Cro-Magnon Man spends many an hour practicing to throw. For he is a meat eater. He lives by what he kills. And nowadays sometimes the hunting is good and sometimes it isn't.

He puzzles a lot about that. Why should the hunting be sometimes good and sometimes not? Isn't there a way to make the animals always abundant? He thinks and he thinks and at last he thinks of a way. You have to use magic. That's the secret— magic. You imitate what Nature does, and you will cause Nature to do that thing. If you make a picture of a lot of mammoths or horses or bison, Nature will produce a lot of mammoths and horses and bison.

So he draws their pictures. He puts them on any good wall space he can find. It doesn't matter that it's in the dark. Darkness is all the better, darkness makes the magic stronger.

At Altamira he paints bison on the ceiling of a pitch-dark chamber. At La Mouthe he engraves them in a tunnel along with ibex and reindeer and horse. At Combarelles he puts nearly the whole animal kingdom he knows on the walls of a dark gallery 720 feet long. At Pasiega he braves the dangerous depths of a cavern underneath his grotto floor. He paints 50 deer there, 51 horses, 16 cattle, 15 bison, 12 stags, 9 ibexes, and so on and so on—226 paintings in all.

Proper wall space is hard to find. Sometimes he has to put one animal on top of another. In a gallery at Font de Gaume he puts whole processions of animals on top of one another. First he puts on a row of reindeer and horses. Later he comes back and puts a row of bison on top of them. Then on top of the bison he puts a procession of mammoths.

He draws and paints and engraves. He learns to make the animals so real they look alive.

He carves animal statuettes. He learns to model clay. In the cavern Tuc d'Audoubert he models two yard-long bison—a male and a female. Everything is for the same purpose.

He makes magic. He paints and engraves and models to make Nature produce. Sometimes he shows a dart sticking into an animal. Sometimes he makes a downward slash like the blow of a club. For isn't it clear that if you wound the picture of an animal you wound the living animal, too? That's how magic works.

It is a wonderful idea. It is one that never quite dies after Cro-Magnon Man has thought it up. Thousands of years later Man will still believe it. He will make a little wax image of his enemy and stick it full of pins. Or melt it in a flame. Or he will stuff his enemy's clothes with straw and hang or burn the image. If you hurt the image, you hurt the man. Isn't that clear? That's magic. That's how it works.

Cro-Magnon Man has a lot of time to think up magic as he sits by his fire and the snow falls fast. He thinks up very strong hunting magic. That's for the eve of the hunt, when you want to make sure of success on the morrow.

The women and children know nothing about that, of course—magic is a business for men. The women and children are all asleep in the front part of the cave. But deep inside, in the farthest, blackest chamber, the men are making magic. Some of the older boys are there, too. They hold the lamps high so the spearmen can see to make their magic.

And well it is that the women and children sleep, for strong hunting magic is a fearful thing to see. There is a great bear in the center of the chamber. The bear is made of clay. He stands on his hind legs, looking so real that it makes your breath come fast. Only instead of a clay head, a real bear's skull sits on top of the heavy neck.

Noiselessly now the Medicine Man steals from the shadows. His body and thighs are striped like an animal's pelt. On his head he wears a stag's horns. Over his face is an owl mask. His ears are a wolf's, his hands are a lion's paws, his tail is the tail of a horse. Only his beard and his legs and feet are human.

With a queer, trotting step he advances. "Be confident!" he seems to say. "Have no fear of the beasts tomorrow. See! Man is fleet as the horse and the stag. His blow is powerful as the lion's. His hearing is sharp as the wolf's. His eyes can pierce the darkness like the owl. He is all that the animals are, and he is also Man, cleverer than any. Be confident!"

He approaches the bear. Now his arms are spread wide—he is beckoning the spearmen to come forward.

And with a rush they come. Brandishing their spears, uttering their hunting cries, they leap into a wild dance around the bear. The Medicine Man also dances. He is fleet as the stag, he is strong as the lion, he is tireless as any of the young men. On the limestone walls his monstrous shadow dances, too.

But all at once the circle breaks—it is time to perform the final magic.

Spear in hand the leader faces the bear. "Cast! Cast!" Behind him the spearmen shout impatiently. Everyone is eager to show his hunting skill. "Cast!"

The leader hurls his spear. And at once the air is filled with hurtling spears, the air is filled with cries. Thirty spears have struck the bear. One has sent the skull clattering down the stalagmite floor.

Dead! The beast is dead! Rejoice! The bear is slain!

The magic is finished. The spearmen can go home and sleep now. The trembling lamp bearers can go home and sleep—if they can. Tomorrow there will be good hunting. Tomorrow there will be meat.

17. Between the Acts

WHEN HE THOUGHT UP HIS MAGIC, CRO-MAGNON MAN
believed he really had the food problem solved.
But not all his lifelike painting and engraving and
modeling could bring the animals to life. Gone was
the mammoth, gone the woolly rhinoceros, gone the
bison, nobody knew where. Much worse, the reindeer was moving northward.

What was to be done? The Mighty Hunter had

become so dependent on the creature he felt lost without the reindeer. Could he do anything other than follow it northward into the cold?

"Leave not the caves of your fathers," some of the old men said. "Better hunger than seek new hunting grounds." And the timid among the young men answered, "We will stay. We will hunt the stag and the roe-deer. We will hunt the wild boar and the wildcat and the hare."

Not everybody had the courage to go.

"There is shellfish on the shores of the sea," some of the old men said. "They who bring us sea shells have said it. They tell of oysters and many-footed crabs and lobsters that make good eating. And the stormy sea casts up great fish. Let us go there."

So some followed the reindeer and some stayed on in the caves and some went to eat shellfish by the sea. And the great life of the caves died. The curtain came fluttering down—Man the Mighty Hunter, Man the Great Artist, passed from the scene.

But the spirit of Man is no simple thing. It is many-sided, it is deathless. This creature has something inside him that will not let him be satisfied with things as they are. His wonderful hands and his wonderful brain give him no rest.

Behind the curtain that has fallen, the scenery

is being shifted. New actors are getting ready to come on. For the Old Stone Age is dying and the New Stone Age is about to be born. But in between the acts, three times the spirit of Man flames high.

He takes clay from the river bank. He mixes it with sand. He shapes a pot and sets it near the fire. And see! It hardens and will not fall apart or crumble. He has a vessel for water and for cooking. He can eat growing things he couldn't eat before.

His clumsy pot seems wonderful to him. He doesn't know that for ages now along the Nile in Africa, along the Tigris and Euphrates in Asia, people have been making much better pots than his. He wonders why he never thought to make this wonderful thing of clay before. Now he will never let it go. In time to come scholars will trace his footsteps by the pots he leaves behind him.

A second time the flame leaps high—and he invents the bow and arrow. It is a stroke of genius. The spear, after all, came from the stick. And the atlatl was just a longer arm. But this is something so original it seems to him to have come right out of the air itself. But no. Everything comes from something else. Perhaps he got the idea from the way a bent branch springs back. Perhaps it made him think of the way the arm throws a stone. Or maybe he got the idea from that little bow the youngsters play with because they like the music it makes when they twang the string.

And what a difference in hunting the bow and arrow make! There isn't half the danger now. You can shoot from four or five hundred yards and hit your mark. The beast can't scent you—you're too far away. It stands there calmly grazing. Then whang! and there's your arrow in its side.

For a third time the flame leaps high—Man domesticates the dog. It is the first of the long line of beasts that will become his servant.

Man doesn't remember now whether he first won the creature over with a tasty bone or whether of its own accord the animal attached itself to him. But from the start they both knew they were made to spend their lives together. Man was just what the dog needed—a master. The dog was just what Man needed—a servant. And now that it is trained to hunt, what a team they make together!

Just watch them following the stag. The stag is fleet, but the dog is fleet, too. The stag is running for its life, but the dog is tireless and will not give up the chase. Does the quarry dash into the leafy thicket? The dog smells it out. The dog won't let the creature hide, he will not let it rest. And when the stag at last is brought to bay, the dog will hold it there.

A strange and marvelous partnership this between the dog and Man. The dog is the perfect servant— it has no will but its master's will. It is more pleased with the master's praise than with the bones and warm place by the fire that are its rightful due. And this is just the beginning of its service. Today it guards Man's home, his wife, his child, is ready to die defending them. Tomorrow it will guard Man's sheep and cattle and give its life defending them.

Behind the curtain the scenes have been shifted. The stage is newly set. The glaciers have been moved to the regions where they are today. Forests have replaced the grasslands. Europe is warm and dry. And into it from the east and south, in wave after wave new actors come. Tall men, short men, long heads, round heads, fair skinned, swarthy men —all of them Homo *sapiens,* Wise Men. But they aren't very wise yet. They are very young. They are very curious. They want to know everything. They want to share in everything that's going on in this fair land of forests and lakes and streams.

The curtain has risen on the New Stone Age, on the Age of Polished Stone.

18. Enter the Farmer

THE RING OF A STONE AX RESOUNDS THROUGH THE forest—Man is chopping down a tree. Listen to that echoing sound! You've scarcely heard it in these parts before. The ax has been in Europe only since the forests came, and this kind, with the cutting edge ground smooth and polished, is just now beginning to get around.

Watch how Man swings the stag-horn handle high. See how he brings the stone head down with all his body's force. It is no easy job to cut a tree down with an ax of stone. And he has chosen a fine, young oak to fell. For it is to be the roof-tree of his house.

Already the house pit has been dug, and he can tell you that with a stag-horn pick and shoulder-blade shovel that was no easy task either. But this sturdy fellow isn't one to quarrel with his tools. Nobody in Europe has any better ones than his. He remembers the old unhafted flints his great-great-great-grandfather used and thinks himself lucky to have the latest models. Those rough old flints just wore you down, blistered your hand till it was hard as horn inside. A handle, now—be it of horn or bone or wood—isn't that a wonderful invention? You can get your whole body's strength behind a tool that has a handle.

He swings and chops, swings and chops, and at last the timber falls. He shouts—and his young sons come running to help carry home the prize.

They set it upright in the very center of the round

pit. And now there's just the umbrella-like roof to make. They fasten poles to the top of the roof-tree. They spread the poles apart, letting them rest on the wall of dirt that came out of the pit. They lay thatch over all—and there's the house ready. The family will need a ladder to get in and out by, but there's this advantage: a wild beast will think twice before leaping down into such a house as this.

This pit house isn't alone on the sunny hillside. A couple of dozen other families are living here in houses just like this. Together they've built a double wall of sharpened posts around their village. At night the dogs give the alarm if enemies approach or beasts come after the cattle.

For Man has cattle now. Yes, and goats and sheep. He brought the creatures with him from abroad. Long, long ago, somewhere in the Near East, those animals were tamed. They are Man's servants over half the earth now.

And what a wonderful thing it is, what a magic thing, this keeping and breeding of beasts! If the hunting fails, Man doesn't go hungry as once he did. There is his meat, right in his pasture. He can slaughter an ox at will—or a goat or a sheep. How Cro-Magnon Man, the Mighty Hunter and Artist, would have opened his eyes at the sight of that pasture! Magic indeed! Man of the New Stone Age has hit upon a better magic than his. He has taken things right out of Nature's hands. He has become his own food producer. And he is making a better job of it than ever Nature did.

See those little fields of wheat and barley and millet. They are man-made. Man is a planter now. He makes ten stalks of grain grow where Nature grew but one or none before. He stirs the ground up with a stag-horn plow, he plants and waits for the grain to ripen. He harvests it with his clumsy flint-toothed sickle. He spreads the grain on a saddle-back stone and with another stone rubs it into flour. He bakes bread.

Say it with reverence—bread. It is the beginning of great things. It is an invention that comes from far. Back in the Near East where it was born, cities with temples and palaces are rising because there is bread in plenty. And all that Man will achieve here in the West will likewise rest upon loaves of bread.

A great revolution has taken place, great things are in the making. Man the Hunter is well on the way to becoming Man the Farmer. He hunts and fishes still—he will always do that—but he no longer simply lives off Nature. Man has become the master of his fate.

It makes a lot of difference. There is less fear

in the world and more confidence. Man can plan ahead, he can live not from day to day and hand to mouth but year to year. He is not afraid to raise a big family—he knows he can provide food enough for all. There are children all around him now.

Yes, the earth's population is growing fast. Time was when there were just little handfuls of people —a few here, a few there—little handfuls of several different kinds of Man. Now there is only one kind of Man on earth, but there are millions of him. In a single land there are perhaps a thousand villages like this.

But they are not all like this.

19. Mystery of the Piles

THE WINTERS OF 1853 AND '54 WERE VERY COLD AND
dry in Europe. In Switzerland the rivers shrank to
narrow ribbons. The lakes dropped till they had less

water in them than the oldest inhabitant could remember. Folk living on the lakefronts looked out of
their windows and wondered, for in front of every
house there was a stretch of land that hadn't been
there before.

Near Ober-Meilen on Lake Zurich some of the
lakefront people got an idea. Why couldn't they
build a wall around a piece of the new waterfront
land, bring up the level a bit, and have a much bigger garden by every house?

Why not?

Stone was carted, mortar mixed. A wall went up.
The lakefront people started dredging mud from
the shore just beyond.

And now what was their astonishment when down
in the mud they came upon wooden posts. Not two
or three or a dozen, but hundreds of posts, thousands. Who drove them into the lake bottom? And
what ever for?

There they were, rows and rows of piles, evenly
spaced a foot or a foot and a half apart, going right
out into the lake. Down at the bottom end the posts
were all charred by fire and sharpened like pencils.
The marks of some very dull sort of ax could be seen
where the piles had been sharpened.

And that wasn't all. In the mud were all sorts

of unexpected things besides—stag antlers, for instance. And bones of oxen and sheep and goats and little long-legged pigs. Also bones of foxes and wolves and martens and other wild beasts. And pieces of crude pottery. And arrowheads and various pieces of polished stone.

What could it all mean?

Mr. Aeppli of Ober-Meilen packed up some of the polished stones and some bits of pottery and took them to Zurich to the Historical Society. These things, he declared, had been made by the unknown men who had driven the piles into the lake. If scientists would search the lake, they would doubtless get valuable information about the early inhabitants of Switzerland.

So the scientists began to search. At first what they found seemed quite unbelievable. On top of the piles here on their own familiar Lake Zurich, platforms had once lain, and on the platforms houses had stood. Four thousand years ago an unknown people had lived out on their lake and then had mysteriously disappeared.

"But why would people want to build a village over our lake?" the citizens of Ober-Meilen wanted to know.

"Protection," the scientists answered. "From ene-

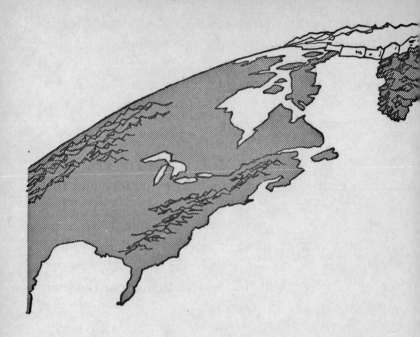

mies and wild beasts. People do just the same thing today, don't you know. Look at Borneo. It's built entirely on the water.

"What's more," the scientists continued, "listen to what Herodotus, the famous Greek traveler, says about the ancient Paeonians. 'Their dwellings are contrived after this manner: planks fitting on lofty piles are placed in the middle of the lake, with a narrow entrance from the mainland by a single bridge.'"

People looked at the piles and they could indeed

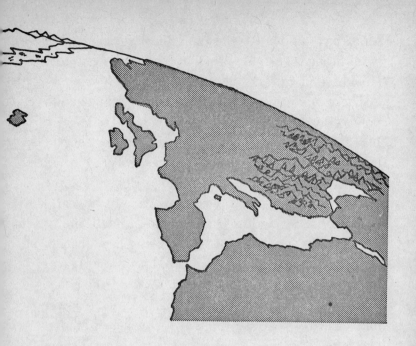

see that a bridge had once led from the shore out into the lake. The pattern of the village began to take shape.

But was Ober-Meilen on Lake Zurich the only place where the Lake Dwellers had lived?

The scientists started dredging every lake bottom in the country. And in one after another they came on piles. Twenty, thirty, forty and more settlements had been scattered along the edges of the larger lakes.

Wonderful treasures began to pour into the museums as the scientists put their finds together. Some were Stone Age things that had never been found anywhere in Europe before.

There were wooden combs, for instance, and bowls and dippers and knives of wood. There were bits of cloth and cord and even straw matting. Not everything, to be sure, was from the days of polished stone. People had lived on the lakes right up to the time of iron. But so many remains were of the early days that it seemed as if the whole intimate life of Man of the New Stone Age was being dredged up.

It was wonderful to watch the story grow. It was like working out a mystery. Here were the piles, for instance. Why were they charred at the lower end? Clearly because the Lake Dwellers found it easier to burn their trees down than to chop them down.

The bones had their own story to tell. When they were sorted out into the different kinds of animals, you could tell at once which creatures the Lake Dwellers had domesticated and which ones they hunted. For *all* the bones of oxen and goats and sheep and pigs were present. That meant they had been domesticated—they had been killed on the spot. But only certain bones—and always the same ones—of stag and deer and marten and fox came out of the lakes. That clearly meant they had been killed in the woods and only the favorite parts had been carried home.

From the samples of food you could tell nearly everything the Lake Dwellers ate—what they raised, what they gathered wild, what they cooked.

It was the same with clothes. Here were bits of hide. Here were knitting needles. Here was flax and a bit of linen cloth, spindle whorls made of clay and a spindle with thread still wound around it. And here were pins to fasten the clothes with.

Thousands of things went into the museums, and all the time a window was opening wider and wider on the home life of the Lake Dwellers. People looked in. The surroundings were strange. But they felt curiously at home just the same.

There was something familiar about this hard-working Man of 2,000 B.C. who was farmer and hunter and fisherman, carpenter, boatwright, tool-maker. There was something familiar about his wife who was miller and baker and spinner and weaver and seamstress and pottery maker. This home which was farm and factory together reminded them of people and times they knew well. Wasn't this just how it had been in America in the early Colonial days?

Of course, the Lake Dwellers lived closer together than the Colonists did. But really all that these folk of the Age of Polished Stone wanted from one another was company and protection. Not one of them had a skill the others didn't. Nobody worked for anybody else. Each family was self-sufficient.

No. There wasn't much call for co-operation here. No big common effort was ever needed—unless it was to put out a fire. So far as doing things together was concerned, Man had actually taken a step backward. Even hunting was something he did pretty much alone now. The animals weren't so big any more—and he had his dog.

20. Stonehenge Goes Up

ON SALISBURY PLAIN IN THE SOUTH OF ENGLAND there is a circle of standing stones. From the ends of the earth people come to look upon this mighty work of Man. They walk around Stonehenge and gape and marvel.

"Who brought these giant stones to stand in solitary grandeur here?" they ask. "And why? What does the circle mean?"

"The Druids built it," people used to say.

But Stonehenge is older than the Druids. It is twice as old as English history itself. Stonehenge is nearly 4,000 years old. When the Stone Age Lake Dwellers were pounding their wooden piles into the lakes of Switzerland, Stonehenge was being built.

For Man is not a simple being. Don't think because his tools are made of stone and bone and horn that he lives by bread alone. He is not everywhere content to be a humdrum householder as on the lakes of Switzerland. There is also something in him that reaches out and lifts him up and gives him wings. You need only look on Stonehenge to know that—it is a monument to the Spirit of Man.

For see! Man has recaptured that way of working together he had when he hunted the mammoth and rhinoceros and bison. He is again joining with his fellows in mighty efforts. From Spain all the way to Scandinavia and throughout the British Isles his spirit soars.

You wouldn't guess, perhaps, to look at this bare-foot fellow dressed in hide, bending over his deer-horn pick and shoulder-blade shovel, that he thinks of anything except how to make himself comfortable in an uncomfortable world. But see all the work he has done for reasons that have nothing to do with his body's comfort.

Those countless great single standing stones scattered through Western Europe—they are his work. He has helped set up many a one—some to mark the resting place of loved relatives, some in memory of great events. And those man-made hills you see everywhere—many a month of his life has gone into piling them up over the tombs of important people.

The biggest job of all, though, was when they built the Sacred Circle on the chalk downs at Avebury. Our barefoot fellow was only a pick-and-shovel man on the mighty job. But the glory of that building is in his eyes.

Would you see the skilled men—the masons, the builders, the architects? Go to Salisbury Plain where Stonehenge is rising and you will see the light is in their eyes, too.

Here is a master builder giving orders at the pit where an upright is being raised. You can feel his confidence. He knows all there is to know about setting up a stone. He has figured out just how deep the hole must be to make this upright come even with the ones on either side. He will make it stand exactly thirteen and a half feet from the ground. He will set it so that it is exactly four feet from its neighbors. He will put it just far enough back so that when the thirty uprights are in place they will make a *perfect* circle.

It is a thrilling moment. Up on the level, men are pushing the twenty-eight-ton stone erect with levers. Others are down in the pit, ready to pile the supporting stones around the giant. This is the last of the great uprights of the outer ring, and the architect looks anxiously to see if his circle is coming exactly right. Everybody is breathing fast.

Steady! Hold it there!

Well done. Now for the sacred blue stones of the inner ring.

In his mind's eye the architect sees his dream complete. He can't wait to have everything in place. Time and again he steps to the spot where the altar stone will lie and looks off into the distance between the two front uprights. That's where the avenue of approach will run. Right there in the center of that avenue he will set one single upright. Then whoever stands on the altar stone like this at dawn on Midsummer's Day and looks down the avenue to the east will see the sun come up exactly over the top of that upright!

The architect is lost in his dream. But all around him the work goes on. Already the master builder is directing his men to dig the pit for the first of the blue stones. The masons are once again busy with chisel and hammer and water and sand. Outside, hundreds of pick-and-shovel men are working on the avenue and on the ditch and bank that will surround the Sacred Circle. There is hustle and bustle and noise and sweat. Stone hammers pound, voices shout orders.

It is a golden moment in the life of the tribe. All the workers sense it. There is joyousness in the air, there is glory in their eyes.

21. Bison Hunt in New Mexico

"AND WHAT ABOUT THE AMERICAS?" PEOPLE ASKED
the scientists. "Tell us. Is Man's story the same in
the New World as in the Old? Did he travel the
same long road up from some unknown American
ape?"

"Oh, no!" the scientists replied in a chorus. "If
there's one thing we are sure of it's that Man in
America didn't spring up from some New World

ape. There are no apes on the double continent for him to have sprung from."

"Then Man *discovered* America? Before Columbus and before the Vikings? Well, then, when would you say Man first got to the New World?"

There was no chorus of answers to that one. Nearly everyone had something different to offer.

"You see, it's this way," one of the scientists explained. "Thirty years back we would have said, 'Not less than three thousand years ago, not more than five.' The idea that Man was a newcomer to America had sort of got frozen in our minds. We had dug and dug, you see, and found no evidence of very ancient people having lived in the New World. But then in 1926 along came Figgins with his thunderbolt. He and his Folsom Man upset everything. . . ."

The scientists nodded their heads. Yes, after Folsom the bottom had dropped right out of their time scale.

As a matter of fact, Jesse Figgins didn't mean to drop a thunderbolt at all. He wasn't even looking for ancient Man. He had gone down to Folsom, New Mexico, with a group of men to dig up bones of extinct animals for the Colorado Museum of Natural History. And he was finding them—bison with great heads and wide-spreading horns like those of a

Texas steer. Then all of a sudden the thunderbolt struck.

"Look here!" one of the scientists cried. They looked, and there he was holding up two pieces of chipped flint!

The men stared at one another dizzily. Those pieces of flint sent Man whirling back through the centuries to the end of the Ice Age, to the time of Cro-Magnon Man!

"You got the flints out of the loose dirt," Figgins managed to say at last. "But we've got to locate one in place if we want people to believe in our 'find.'"

They returned to their search. And there, imbedded in the clay around a bison rib, lay a piece of chipped flint!

Very carefully the men cut out the entire block of clay—ribs, flint, everything—and sent it to the museum laboratory. What excitement there was then! When the flint was lifted from the clay, everyone could see it was the other half of one of the broken ones and that together the two bits made a point for a dart.

Yet scarcely a scientist would accept the idea that the bison had met his death at the hands of Man.

"How, then, did the flint get between the bison's ribs?" the museum people demanded.

"We don't know how," the scientists answered. "It's just one of those things. It slipped in from the surface—somehow. Maybe through an animal hole —or something."

Figgins got mad. "I'll show them!" he said and went right back to Folsom.

An idea had struck him. He had found so many bison bones all in one place. Didn't that mean, perhaps, that Man had ambushed and killed them all on this spot? And if Folsom really was the scene of an ancient hunt, wouldn't he find some more dart points among the bones?

Just as he thought, so it happened. He hadn't been digging long before another broken point appeared, then three more. But as luck would have it, each was loosened from the clay before its exact position could be marked. A fifth point finally appeared, however. And this time it was firmly imbedded in the clay.

Figgins was satisfied. The flint lay exactly on the same level as the bison bones—which was all the evidence he needed. He immediately sent telegrams to the leading scientific institutions and sat down to wait for visitors.

They came. From three great institutions scientists hurried to Folsom. And this time they believed. "We are convinced," they announced, "that Folsom

Man lived at the end of the Ice Age and hunted the extinct bison."

For quite a while scientists struggled against the idea. But in the end nearly all of them accepted it. Five thousand years? No. Perhaps they would have to multiply by as much as five the thousands of years they had given Man in the New World. Folsom and Cro-Magnon Man had shared the earth between them. At one and the same time on different sides of the Atlantic each had hunted the great beasts of his land.

22. Did They Do It All Alone?

ONCE THEY GOT USED TO THE IDEA, MOST OF THE scientists were relieved to be able to push American Man back to the end of the Ice Age.

"It always bothered us to have to squeeze him into just three to five thousand years," they confessed. "We saw him coming from Asia across Bering Strait. We saw him spreading from the tip of Alaska to the tip of South America. We saw him occupying the land from the Pacific to the Atlantic.

That must have taken a good many thousand years.

"Things happened to him on the way, too. He was used to living in the freezing cold, but now he learned to take any kind of climate Nature offered. He made his home in the everlasting snows, but also where it is torrid hot and never snows. He got used to living where it rains all the time and where it never rains at all. He learned to get along at sea level and 14,000 feet up on the mountain heights.

"His body changed, too. There are more differences among Indians in height and color and features than there are among white men. And his numbers grew amazingly. From little handfuls here and there, Man increased till he could be counted in the millions.

"Then there was language. The Indians don't all speak one tongue. They have 1,200 different languages—including the dialects. How many thousand years must it have taken to develop so many!

"And finally there were Mexico and Central America and Peru. We always felt we weren't giving those wonderful civilizations time enough to develop. We figured Man came from Asia with hands almost bare and with very little know-how in his head. He had clothes of some kind. He had the spear and spear-thrower. He knew how to chip flint. He could make fire. Later he came again and brought the bow. He brought the dog. He brought the know-how to make a rude boat. But everything else he had to develop in the New World. And it is a very long way from a chipped flint to a pyramid temple."

Not all the scientists, however, felt relieved. Some of the die-hards tried desperately to hold on to 3,000 B.C. But while they argued others went off to follow up more clues of Folsom Man. The noise of Figgins' thunderbolt had hardly died before they were out in the field. Such a searching began as had never been seen in America before.

Folsom Man, the scientists soon discovered, had lived all over the High Plains on the eastern slope of the Rockies. And cousins of his had certainly lived very near him. For at Yuma, Colorado, quantities of their handsome flints were dug up. In fact, these cousins seemed to have left flints far and wide— all the way up to Canada and even Alaska.

But as for Folsom Man himself, not a scrap of bone could the scientists find.

It was very disappointing.

"But really not surprising," the scientists said. "Folsom Man was a hunter. He didn't live in a cave and he didn't stay in any one place long. So it is very unlikely that he buried his dead."

"Yes, and under such circumstances," one scientist pointed out, "it would be only by the merest chance that you would come across a Folsom skeleton. And even if you did, you very likely couldn't tell it was one."

"Then perhaps," someone suggested, "Folsom Man has already been found only nobody recognizes that it is Folsom Man."

The scientists thought a moment about that. "There really is one skeleton that may possibly go back that far," they admitted at last.

They were thinking about the Minnesota Man whose bones some road menders had found in a place that had once been a glacial lake.

"We don't know what the Minnesota skeleton was," one scientist said cautiously, "except that it was not a man's but a young girl's. She may have been Folsom. But then, again, she may have been Sioux. When we do find Folsom Man, we probably won't know it, though. Nothing but Homo *sapiens* has ever been found in the New World and it's our conviction that nothing but Homo *sapiens* ever will. Probably we won't be able to see much more than that the skull is beetle-browed and long-headed rather than round. Most of the older skeletons we find are that way. On that account some of us are even coming around to the idea that the first men in America weren't Indians at all but . . ."

"Not Indians!"

"No, not Indians at all but Australoids."

"Australoids! What's that?"

"Well, they are the kind of people whom the white men found in Australia when they discovered that continent. The Australian bushmen are all long-headed and their brow-ridges are more marked than ours. They may be closer descendants of Neander-thal Man than we are."

As a matter of fact, what Folsom Man looked like concerned the scientists less than something else. They were troubled by what they called the *gap*. They couldn't understand it. Here on one hand was Folsom Man, a rude savage, chipping flint, having no pottery, raising no food. And here on the other hand were the wonderful Maya of Central America and Yucatán, the Aztecs of Mexico, and the Incas of Peru.

"What happened in between?" the scientists wondered. "Where are the steps by which Man climbed?"

Some people refused to believe the Indians had learned everything by themselves and in such a short time. "It is impossible," they said. "Nobody can be that smart. Boatloads of people from the Old World must have come across the Pacific and taught them."

Some pointed to pictures. "Look at these portraits of Central American gods," they said. "Do they look like Indians? No. They have a beard. Indians have no beards. Doesn't that prove that white men came and taught them?"

"White men? Certainly white men," one scientist said. "And I will tell you who those white men were. They were the sailors of Alexander the Great. Remember? He built a navy of 800 ships. What happened to it? Doubtless after his death it sailed out of the Persian Gulf, down the coast of India, and on to the Pacific Islands. There it picked up a lot of Polynesians and took them along. Together they discovered America."

It was a very exciting idea. Could it possibly be true?

Some cautiously ventured to say, "It explains a good many things."

Others said, "Yes, but there are a lot of things it doesn't explain. If the sailors taught the inhabitants how to make pottery, why didn't they also teach them how to make the potter's wheel? Alexander's men would certainly have known about that. And how to smelt metals. The Peruvians knew how, but they didn't learn it till much, much later."

"Yes, and writing," someone else added. "Why didn't the sailors teach the Maya Greek writing?

Or Egyptian? Surely they wouldn't have sat down and invented an altogether new kind. And the calendar. The Maya calendar was more accurate than any the Old World had till just a few centuries ago. The sailors couldn't have brought that with them. Did they stop everything else and sit down to invent the terribly complicated Maya calendar? And zero. Nobody in the Old World had a sign for zero at that time. So the sailors couldn't have brought it with them. Did they invent the zero, too?"

"No," others said. "That's not very likely. And if you once admit that the Maya invented zero and the calendar, then you don't need the Greek sailors at all. A people who could invent those two wonderful things could easily invent everything else. Everything else the Old World also had and some things it didn't. The hammock, for instance. The cigar, cigarette, and tobacco pipe. Hollow rubber balls. Elastic rings. Toboggans. And a few wonderful things besides."

"Corn and potatoes, for example."

"Yes, those. Corn and potatoes."

23. Hats Off!

SAILORS AREN'T SUPPOSED TO UNDERSTAND FARMING but even if Alexander's sailors did, it was clear to everybody they didn't teach anything in that line to the Indians. On that the scientists were all agreed.

"Look at corn," they said. "When Columbus landed in 1492, the Indians were raising more than 700 different varieties of it. They developed all of them from a single parent plant. How long do you suppose it took them to do it?"

"Twenty thousand years," one botanist said.

"Oh, no. That's too long," another argued.

"Corn is certainly very old," someone else put in. "It has even lost the power of taking care of itself —unless somebody plants it and takes care of it, it won't grow. But we have to remember also that before corn there were beans and squash and manioc and potatoes and cotton."

The scientists could see American farming going back and back and back. For not all the early Americans, it seemed, were hunters. When after Figgins' thunderbolt the scientists started following up clues of early Man, they came on a most amazing "find." Way back even before the end of the Ice Age, American Man had ground things on milling stones!

"We don't mean to say that Man ground corn on those milling stones, of course," the scientist who found them hastened to explain. "What those stones mean is that very long ago there were food gatherers in America as well as hunters. Doubtless it was such people who became the first farmers."

"And once they started, there was no stopping

them!" one botanist exclaimed with admiration. "Think of v.hat they did to create the potato! To get it they probably crossed nightshade and Jimson weed and tobacco and quite a number of other plants."

"Yes, and they created the seedless pineapple, too," another added.

"Oh, that's much less wonderful than what they did to get tapioca from manioc," someone else said. "When they discovered that one variety of manioc was poisonous, they wove a special press that would squeeze the poison out and leave the wholesome starch behind."

There was no doubt about it. Man in America, everybody had to grant, had been the most original and remarkable farmer in the world. He had discovered and developed more than twenty food plants. Besides three kinds of beans, squash, pumpkin, corn, manioc, and white potatoes, he raised sweet potatoes and chili peppers, tomatoes and pineapple, peanuts and strawberries, avocados and Jerusalem artichokes, sunflower seeds and custard apples, cacao (for chocolate) and several other food plants. He raised New World cotton and tobacco. And he made use of all sorts of things that grew wild.

He harvested persimmons and papaws and papayas and guavas and plums and cherries and cashew nuts and wild rice. He dug arrowroot and picked maté for tea. He drew the latex from the hevea tree and made rubber. He took the resin copal and made varnish out of it. He made gum from chicle. From cinchona bark he got quinine to cure fever. He gathered the leaves of the coca shrub to chew fatigue away. From anil he made indigo dye. He found that certain insects called cochineal could be dried and crushed and made into red dye. So he raised those insects.

"All these things early Man in America passed on to the world," the scientists said with awe.

They were thinking of corn waving on every continent of the world but one. They were thinking of potatoes saving the lives of the starving Irish, feeding Europe, creeping farther and farther north all the time. They were thinking of the millions of cans of pineapple and tomatoes and beans on grocery shelves, of cigarettes and rubber tires and indigo dye. They were thinking of peanut butter and chocolates and chewing gum and strawberry jam.

"Perhaps the Indians of Mexico and Central America and Peru didn't develop their civilizations all by themselves," one of the scientists said thoughtfully. "But really it isn't of any importance. What they did as farmers is quite enough for any people. I, for one, will take my hat off to the Indians."

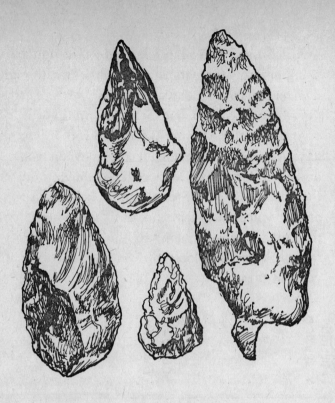

24. On the Shoulders of Stone Age Man

EAST OF THE MISSISSIPPI TO THE APPALACHIAN MOUN-
tains, from Wisconsin to the Gulf of Mexico lie the
mounds of America. There are a hundred thousand
of them. Some are huge, covering many acres. Some
are smaller.

All of them were built by Man. And no one remembers who that Man was. Even when the white men first moved westward across the Alleghenies, the Mound Builders had been forgotten.

And yet the Mound Builders lived just yesterday. At least, that's how it seems when you look down the long road Man covered moving up from the ape to the New Stone Age. It will strike you at once if you stop to look. So let us make a picture of that road. A road as long as this page is wide will represent for us Man's life on earth—one million years at most.

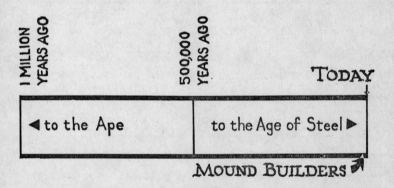

There it is. There is our road. A million years of human beings. A million years of effort. Almost a million years of slow plodding along. There at the very end are the Mound Builders. See how they rub shoulders with Man of Today?

On the Shoulders of Stone Age Man

Now let us divide this road into the Old Stone Age and the New Stone Age. See how long a time must be given to the Old Stone Age. See how late the farmer comes on the stage.

Next let us try to place upon this million-year long road the heroes of our book. We will put them only approximately where they belong. For we can't do it exactly. We have to guess at a lot. Certainly we have to place a question mark before the time of the Giant Ape-Man. And certainly we aren't at all sure of where the Little Java Ape-Man or Peking Man go. But the farther along we get, the surer we can be.

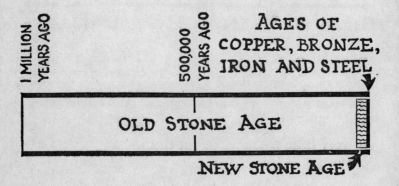

There it is—our Time Chart of Man. You see how crowded it gets at the end. There is no room to put Man of the Age of Iron and Steel on at all. The line that ends the road must stand for us. As you see, the Lake Dwellers of 4,000 years ago tread right on our toes. That's because we know more about the people who lived closest to us. We can put more of them in.

You will note that there is a very long empty space between Peking Man and Neanderthal Man.

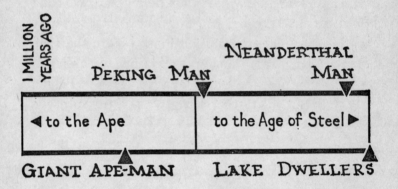

But actually that piece of road wasn't empty. There are a couple of fellows who belong in there. Scientists call them Abbévillian Man and Acheulian Man. We said nothing about them in this book because so very little is known about them.

We know what their tools were like—Boucher de Perthes picked up a lot of them. Mostly they were flint core hatchets. And we know that these fellows liked warm weather because in Europe their tools are found together with the bones of warmth-loving animals like the hippopotamus. But we don't know what they looked like. There are too few bones to go on. All we have is parts of five or six skulls and a jawbone. We get a hint of what one of those fellows was like from the great size of that jaw. But we don't know much more.

Well, that's approximately where our heroes belong. See how short a time it is since Cro-Magnon Man came into Europe. Yet in that little while, in those little more than 25,000 years, there was more progress than in all the 975,000 that went before.

But now let us make a different kind of chart. Let us think of Man's greatest inventions and try to place them in that million years. What will our chart look like? Something like this:

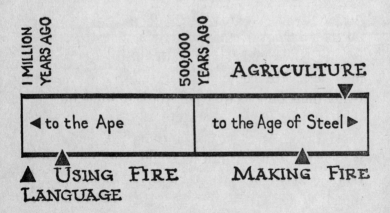

What? Are language, fire, and agriculture Man's greatest inventions?

Yes. Language, fire, and agriculture are Man's supreme inventions. Beside them his atlatl and his bow are as nothing. His needles and his pots and his house and his boat and his loom are as nothing. Beside them all our steam boats and automobiles and jet planes, our television and atom splitting are as nothing. For upon language, fire, and agriculture rest everything else Man has accomplished. These three are the base on which we have built. These three we owe to Stone Age Man whose very existence we doubted less than a hundred years ago. We stand on the shoulders of Stone Age Man.

Take language. What would Man be without it? Why, for all his big brain, for all his erect posture, without language Man would be hardly better than a beast. He couldn't communicate with his fellows. He couldn't join with them in any common task. He couldn't even think. For we can really think only as we have words to think in.

Next, take fire. Without fire Man could have no cooked food. Without fire he could live only where it is warm. Without fire he could work only while there is daylight. Without fire he couldn't smelt metal. Which means, of course, that he would forever be chained to wood and bone and shell and stone. Stonehenge would be as much, perhaps, as he would ever have achieved.

Last, take agriculture.

We call agriculture the Mother of Civilization. For see. Without agriculture there is no building, and without building there is no city life, and without city life there is no civilization.

It is agriculture that makes it possible for Man to be sure of his food supply. It is an assured food supply that makes his numbers increase greatly. With numbers comes leisure—for a few can raise enough food for the many and the rest can turn hand and mind to something else. Some can acquire special skills. Others still can think and plan and invent for the rest.

Most important, agriculture makes it possible for Man to stay in one place generation after generation. And that is the seed from which the arts spring. For as long as Man is a hunter who moves around from place to place, he will rarely create fine things. Remember that Cro-Magnon Man the Artist didn't move around. He lived in one place—and when he started to move around, his art died.

For what is the good of painting and sculpture if you're off somewhere else next season? What is the good of building a fine house and putting beautiful things in it when you have to leave them behind?

But as soon as people have a food they can depend on—a cereal food like wheat or rice or corn, say—they can settle down and start building things that will last. The arts develop. Religion begins to play a greater part. Temples spring up. Paintings and statues are made. Writing is invented. Cities are born.

Until you have agriculture progress is slow. Once you have agriculture, Man moves along by leaps and bounds. That's how it was with the first men in the world.

For hundreds of thousands of years Man crept along. All he had by way of the arts was a crude form of language. His sole comfort was fire. He took it where he found it. Slowly he learned to hunt. Painfully he learned to chip flint. For hundreds of thousands of years he did almost nothing but hunt and chip. Then he learned how to make fire. Very late, almost at the very end, he invented the atlatl, the bow, domesticated the dog, learned to make pots. Finally came agriculture. And agriculture was the great beginning.